Grace,

My Dearest Friend

Cheryl Elliott
Micah 6:8

BY
CHERYL ELLIOTT

PROFESSIONAL PUBLISHING MEETS POWERFUL PROMOTION

A wholly owned subsidary of TBN

My Dearest Friend
Trilogy Christian Publishers A Wholly Owned Subsidary of Trinity Broadcasting Network
2442 Michelle Drive Tustin, CA 92780

Manufactured in the United States of America
10 9 8 7 6 5 4 3 2 1
Library of Congress Cataloging-in-Publication Data is available.
ISBN: 978-1-68556-827-6
E-ISBN: 978-1-68556-828-3

Dedication

This book is dedicated to my parents, Roy and Shirley Sandefur, who instilled in me from a very young age a love of God and His Word. The older I get, the more I realize how blessed I am to have had not only godly parents but grandparents as well.

Preface

I believe the study of Scripture should be fresh and exciting—never boring! I also believe that we modern-day women are a lot more like Bible-time women than we realize. It is for these two reasons that these letters have been written.

As a life-long student of the Bible and a graduate of Johnson University in Knoxville, Tennessee, it is my passion to equip women more fully in the study and application of scripture. Being able to identify with the problems and circumstances of women in the past and learning life lessons through their experiences can help us maneuver through our own trials and heartaches in the present.

It is my prayer that, as you curl up with these letters from Old Testament women, you will come away with a better understanding of not only their lives in general but their hearts in particular. Realize, too, that I've taken a lot of liberty in writing these letters and have imaginatively filled in the blanks about how each of these Bible-time women may have thought and felt. From childlessness to wayward children, from disobedience to idol worship, from jealousy to fears to insecurities, we all have issues we struggle to maneuver through almost daily. We would do well to listen to the advice these Bible-time women have to offer. Consider them a mentor helping you along your life's journey. Ultimately, I hope to take these women away from the black-and-white sketches of the past and bring them into full-color, life-sized portraits in the present.

May God bless you as you get to know these Old Testament Bible-time women on a deeper and more personal level.

Cheryl

Acknowledgments

My love relationship with God and His Word may have begun at my parents' knees, but it has grown and been enriched over the years through interaction with a countless number of men and women. If our paths crossed for more than fifteen minutes, know that you have had a part in the writing of this book because, in some way, you left an imprint on my heart. Thank you.

With that being said, allow me to recognize a handful of men and women who have prayed me through the writing of this current book of letters and/or gone above and beyond in their words of encouragement.

The "top three" women in my life: my daughter, Stasie; my granddaughter, Haley; and my sister, Georgia. I consider these women to have been the biggest influencers in shaping me into the person I am today. These are the ladies with whom I'm in almost daily (if not daily) contact—and have been for years. Thank you for allowing me to grow. And, especially, thank you for your restraint in not sharing with the world all my secrets and insecurities.

The men in my life: my brother, David; my sons, Phillip and Benjamin; and my son-in-law, Randy. Words cannot begin to express how much I appreciate their encouragement, prayers, and support. I must also give a big thank you to Kelvin, who has challenged me this past year in so many ways. He has not let me get by with anything—and for that, I'm so very grateful.

The "other women" in my life: my sister, Brenda; my sister-in-law, Kathy; and my daughter-in-law, Yanique, as well as three very special ladies from my church family—Laura, Sheila, and Gayle. These women are astounding examples of what it means to live life as a godly woman. These are some of the women I would love to be around more often.

I also acknowledge God the Father, Son, and Holy Spirit. I readily admit that, without Him, I would be nothing. It is because of His gifting, His prompting, and His guidance that these letters found their way onto the written pages of this book. All praise to God for His abundant grace, mercy, forgiveness, and love. Thank you to my Rock. My Foundation. My Creator. "Give thanks to the Lord for He is good. His love endures forever" (Psalm 136:1, NIV).

Table of Contents

Eve

Poor Choices, Painful Consequences

Eve's story is found in Genesis 2:15–4:8, 25–26

My Dearest Friend,

I pray this letter finds you well and happy. There is so much I want to share with you about my life. Its ups and downs were many. Its highs and lows extreme. But I learned so much in those experiences. And it is my desire to pass along some of the painful lessons I learned so your life might be a bit easier. Brace yourself—this may be a long letter!

The best place to start is always at the beginning. If you know anything about me at all, you most likely know I was the first woman the LORD God created. What an honor that was! I only wish I had realized it sooner. When I took my first breath, I was already a woman and married, so to speak, to a man named Adam. No childhood. No friends other than God, Adam, and the animals, of course! And no dating, engagement, or wedding ceremony. Some have said I missed out on a lot. Perhaps I did, but the gains were so much more! More on that later.

Without getting too mushy, I'll just say that Adam was ecstatic when he first saw me. He knew immediately that God had created me especially for him—to be his companion. I will admit that I was very pleased with Adam as well. He was perfect for me. He was tall, dark, handsome, and strong! It was when I first laid eyes on him that I realized the beating of my own heart. I know, I promised not to be too mushy…but I couldn't help myself. We were so much in love. We were literally made for each other!

Adam and I spent hours walking hand-in-hand in the Garden of Eden, talking, laughing at the antics of the animals, smelling the flowers, sniffing and tasting the fruits and vegetables, enjoying the gentle breezes, and counting the stars—well, trying anyway! It was an absolute paradise. Everything was simply perfect. It all seems like a dream now…it was so very long ago.

My mind's eye can still picture it. Beauty unlike anything you can imagine. Sounds so peaceful and calming. And God. Did you know that God talked with us all the time—morning, noon, and night? I remember in the mornings God was always so eager for Adam and me to get the day started. Then, at noon, we would sit down, relax among the flowers and trees, and just listen to the birds sing. But I think His favorite part of the day was our evening strolls together—I know they were mine. God truly looked forward to the evening walks He took with us. He always asked us about our day. He wanted to hear what new discoveries we had made or what had caused us to laugh. We would tell Him, and He would laugh along with us and was delighted with every new discovery. I can still hear His laugh the day we told Him about the smell of the skunk! He laughed so hard! That got Adam and me laughing, too. We all laughed so much that our sides hurt, and there were tears running down our faces!

But you know, that was typical of God. He was so much fun to be with, and He was interested in absolutely everything we did. He was always so excited to point out parts of His creation to us as we wandered through the Garden. It was almost as if He couldn't wait for us to see them and enjoy them for ourselves! What a glorious blessing those days were, leisurely walking and talking with God. What an honor. My friend, I wish I knew then what I know now. You see, amid all this beauty and perfection, Adam and I made a horrible mistake. That's the second thing you need to know about me. Let me tell you what happened.

The day started out like every other. I had woken up to birds singing and even a rooster crowing in the distance. I remember being so excited to get the day started—to chat with God and Adam, to see what new discoveries were ahead for that day. As was His custom, God always seemed to show up the minute I woke up. One time I asked Him how He always seemed to do that. He told me it was because He never slept. Instead, He spent those hours watching me and marveling over me and all that He had created. Sometimes the things God said or did took my breath away. This was one of those times.

One day, after Adam and I had enjoyed our morning time with God, we were contentedly strolling through the Garden and into the meadow, admiring the flowers and watching the frisky animals. Today's entertainment feature were young cubs. They were so cute. Adam decided to join in the fun. And, before I knew it, he was rolling around on the ground with a couple of cubs, having the time of his life.

Meanwhile, I was totally unaware that a serpent was approaching me. I had noticed him before, but he always seemed to stay in the distance, just watching Adam and me. To say I was shocked when he first spoke to me would be an understatement. I had no idea he could talk! Since I was standing there flabbergasted, he took the opportunity to start a conversation. He began by casually mentioning the beautiful garden around us, the delicious natural foods that were in abundance, and the refreshing water from a nearby spring. I had to agree with him—everything was wonderful. Then he started talking about and pointing out the various trees around us. One by one, I told him about the fruit each one provided.

Then it happened. He pointed to the tree in the middle of the Garden. I wasn't really surprised that he was especially curious about that one because it did seem to be taller, fuller, and a bolder, more vivid green than any of the other trees. And the color of the fruit on that tree was somehow more colorful, more beautiful, more eye-catching than all the other fruit in the Garden. He asked what I knew about that tree. So, I told him that tree was very special to God and that it was the only one in the Garden which fruit Adam and I were not supposed to eat. He seemed surprised by that fact and kept quizzing me. "Are you sure that's what God said? Perhaps you misunderstood Him." Even though I kept telling the serpent I was sure of what God had said, he always seemed to have another argument or explanation. I honestly had no clue that he was up to no good. He was such a smooth talker. Anyway, the serpent told me that he had a confession to make. He told me that he already knew some very wonderful things about the fruit from that tree—how it tasted so good, better than any other fruit, how it would enrich my life, allowing me to know as much as God, and how it would make me wise, just like God. For a while, the serpent had me so focused on the things I didn't have that I couldn't see the countless good things I did have. I began to resent God for holding out on me. Eventually…well, as you know, I just couldn't resist.

I know what you're probably thinking. In hindsight, I can see how the serpent was planting seeds of doubt in my head until those seeds sprouted. But, at the time, it just sounded so wonderful—and I certainly didn't want to be left out! Then I began to justify what I was about to do. I thought, *What a nice surprise it would be for God to have someone to talk to who was on the same intellectual level as He was.* So, the serpent and I went over to the tree, and I cautiously reached out my hand to pull off a piece of its fruit. And, just like that, I took a bite—not a very big one, mind you, because I wasn't at all sure what would happen or how it would taste. But the serpent was right. It was so juicy and so sweet. And, since nothing bad seemed to happen, I took a piece to Adam so he could enjoy it as well. Just like me, he was a bit hesitant at first to eat it. But I convinced him to try it. That's when it first dawned on me that I was different. Here I was, standing in the Garden, trying to convince Adam to eat the forbidden fruit. I was acting no better than that serpent! For a brief moment, I thought about stopping Adam, but I was too ashamed to admit my mistake. Almost before I knew it, both Adam and I were sitting on the ground under that tree, enjoying its fruit.

It didn't seem to take very long before we both had this sudden change come over us. It was very confusing. And although we didn't know what exactly was happening, we both knew we would never be the same. We began to see each other differently—and we didn't like what we saw or how we felt. We were extremely uncomfortable. It was such an awful feeling. I realized then that the serpent had downright lied to me. He had intentionally deceived me. Oh, he made me so mad! So many new and strange feelings were bombarding Adam and me all at once. Guilt. Shame. Sorrow. Disappointment. We had never felt any of those before we ate the fruit.

As I've had time to reflect, I've often wondered how I could have been so gullible. How I could have allowed the serpent to talk me into doing something that I knew the LORD God had warned against. It was *the lie*. Before that time, I never even knew what a lie was! But I've since learned that my disobedience was as much my fault as it was the lie that led up to it. What I didn't want to admit was that I may have been just a smidgen curious about that tree. Why would God have created something so perfect, put it in the very center of the Garden, and not even allow us to *touch* it? I didn't understand His reasoning. So, in a guilty sort of way, I was perhaps secretly excited to hear all the serpent was telling me about the special tree. And, rather than just trust God, I made the conscious choice to be disobedient.

Adam and I weren't quite sure as to what to do next. We were disappointed in ourselves and embarrassed. For a while, we both just sat there under the tree, trying to decipher thoughts and understand feelings we couldn't seem to wrap our minds around. I remember that among the multitude of seemingly instantaneous thoughts I had, there were two that kept circulating around to the forefront of my mind. First was sadness that I had done something God had specifically told me not to do. And second, I realized I was naked and needed to find a way to hide my body—both from Adam and from God. About the time I began to wonder what Adam was thinking, he jumped up and began pulling off leafy branches from a fig tree nearby to cover us up. Evidently, our thoughts were running along the same path. It wasn't until after we were both covered that we cautiously began to whisper to one another. We had no idea what all the consequences would be of our eating the fruit, but we had experienced enough already to know this probably wasn't going to end well.

For the rest of the afternoon, as was our custom, we wandered the Garden. But this time, there was no joy. The colors seemed to have faded. There were no new discoveries. Even the animals seemed more subdued. We did very little talking. I remember that afternoon everything seemed to have slowed down. Adam and I were walking with a heaviness we had never known before. For the first time in our lives, we were not looking forward to meeting

God for our evening stroll. So, we agreed to hide.

My dear friend, looking back on it now, it seems laughable that we thought we could not only hide from God but hide our actions from Him as well. And, whether we realized it or not at the time, I think we both were hoping "out of sight, out of mind." Perhaps God wouldn't miss us just this once. We were hoping that our situation would be temporary, and by tomorrow morning, everything would be back to the way it had been. So, we decided to hide from God. I'm not sure why. I'm sure we both knew, deep down, that God would find out sooner or later what we had done. As I sit here reflecting on that, I realize how arrogant that was of us.

As you probably already know, God did find us. And, as we suspected, He was extremely disappointed in what we had done. To make matters worse, it took God a while to get us to be completely truthful with Him and tell the whole story about what had happened. But, more than just simply telling the story, Adam and I both wanted God to be very clear as to who was at fault for our disobedience. Adam blamed me; I blamed the serpent. The serpent insisted that he didn't force me—he only "suggested" I eat the fruit. It was quite awkward. We were wrong, and we knew it. But neither Adam nor I nor the serpent (surprise) wanted to admit it. One thing I've learned is that people tend to want to think that if we ignore sin, or hide it, or do it in secret, that everything will be okay. But I'm here to tell you that God will find out. Every time. The smartest thing to do when we sin is to swallow our pride and immediately ask God's forgiveness.

When God finally got us to admit to the truth, He punished us in different ways. He cursed the serpent and caused him to grovel in the dust, crawling on his belly. For me, He said that when I began to have children of my own, it would be extremely painful. God told Adam that he would have to work hard to provide for himself and his family. God was not a happy camper—and neither were we at that point. But you know what God did? Right in the middle of His dishing out punishment, He stopped and killed an innocent animal and made clothes for us from its skin. We were so ashamed and so humbled. To think that an innocent animal had to die because of us! It brought me to tears—and still does.

My friend, let me interject another bit of wisdom here while I'm thinking on it. I've been gone a long time now, and I've both seen and heard a lot of things. But the most important thing of all is that this experience with the innocent animal dying reminds me of the sacrifice Christ made on the cross several thousand years after I roamed the earth. Because we humans are such sinners, there's no way for us to save ourselves. So God sent His Son, Jesus Christ, to this world to save us—to cover our sins. After a few short years of living among us, Jesus willingly died so we could be saved. Mankind had become so sinful that there was no way we could find salvation on our own. It took Jesus Christ and His blood. Talk about being humbled!

Getting back to my story...remember earlier when I said that God paused in the middle of His punishment of Adam and me to make us clothes? Well, as I'm still reeling from the death of the innocent animal, God banished us from the Garden of Eden. That's the only home we had ever known. And at that time, Adam and I weren't sure if we'd ever see or hear or talk with God again. We really had become friends, you know. That's why I know God's heart was breaking, too—maybe even more.

When Adam and I first left the Garden, I deeply missed God's closeness and hearing His genuine concern for us in His voice, His laughter, and seeing the twinkle in His eye. But I soon discovered that no matter where I was, I could talk with Him, and He would talk with me. My not being able to see Him physically with my eyes didn't stop God from reaching out to us. I realized that, even though distance may have separated us, God was big enough to bridge that gap—and He never once failed to do so. He was just as close to us and just as concerned about us after we left the Garden as He always had been.

It took Adam and me a little bit of time to adjust to our new living conditions. However, we realized very quickly that this was going to be our new reality, and we had better make the best of it. So, once we got settled, Adam began to grow food for us and tend the animals. He worked so hard! Day after day, he was out there trying his best to provide for us. Meanwhile, I became pregnant and soon had a whole other new reality to wrap my mind around. I had so many questions as my body began to grow bigger and bigger. What will our baby look like? How will I know when it's time for the baby to be born? How will I know how to take care of a baby? So many questions. So few answers. The only thing Adam and I could do as we learned to maneuver this new reality was to trust God.

When I gave birth to Cain, that's when I fully understood how severe God's punishment was for me. Oh, you talk about excruciating pain! Yet, that baby was worth every bit of it. Adam and I had so much fun watching him grow and learn things like crawling, walking, talking. They do grow up fast, don't they? As it turned out, about the time Cain was just beginning to walk pretty well, I gave birth to Abel. For a time, life seemed to run smoothly. We were busy, but we were happy. Oh, we had our ups and downs, mind you. Being close in age, some days the boys would play together as best friends and other days, well, worst enemies! Sometimes I wanted to pull my hair out in frustration. I may not have known about arguing when I encountered the serpent, but my boys seemed to learn it naturally. And being their mother, I had to learn what you call child psychology as I went along. But they did grow up to become handsome young men—even if I say so myself!

You know, Cain became a great farmer. He had what you would call a "green thumb." Everything just seemed to grow for him. And Abel, well, Abel had a knack for animals. Some would follow him around wherever he went. He always seemed to have them by his side, talking to them, petting them. Oh, how he loved his animals!

I remember, as clearly as if it were yesterday, the second most horrible day of my life. My sons were going through an unusually rugged time of competition between them. You know how boys do—who's fastest, who's strongest, who's smartest. With them, everything seemed to be a competition.

From the time the boys were little, we had told them about God and the Garden of Eden. Adam and I regularly brought sacrificial gifts to God, asking for His forgiveness, thanking Him for continuing to be with us and providing for us. We knew from our days in the Garden that God was in control, and everything belonged to Him. Giving back to Him a small portion of what He'd given us wasn't too much to ask—especially after what we had done. In fact, we were thankful to be able to do it—to ask God's forgiveness and favor. And we did it repeatedly. We didn't want anything to ever come between us and God again. We tried to teach that to the boys and explain to them how it's not the size of the gift that mattered. What was important was that it needed to be a sacrifice—something that was important and cost you the best of what you have. God had sacrificed an animal for us in the Garden, so our custom had been to sacrifice an animal as well. When you give back to God, you're giving because you want to give, not because you must. Heart attitude is so critical. There's so much wrapped up in our attitude toward God when it comes to giving and humbly asking for His forgiveness and mercy.

Anyway, let me tell you what happened. Anyone who has been around children any length of time knows you don't always get the whole story of how or why something happened. You just kind of piece together information and draw your own conclusions. I'm not sure who first suggested they go and offer a sacrifice to God—and it really doesn't matter. But I think Cain may have looked at this as just another big competition. I imagine he saw this as a "let's see who God likes best" opportunity, whereas

Abel was giving as he always had—from his heart. From what I have been able to figure out, I believe Abel gave the best of what he had—a young animal that was spotless and unblemished, just as we had encouraged in our own sacrifices to God. And I believe Cain gave an abundance of the best of the crops he had grown through much time, labor, and sweat.

In hindsight, I wonder if Cain's offering wasn't accepted—not because it wasn't the best of his crops—but because it wasn't a living sacrifice. After all, in the Garden, while Adam and I thought covering ourselves with fig leaves (a type of crop) was enough, God let us know our disobedience and sin required a blood sacrifice. At any rate, I also think Cain's heart wasn't right or that he gave with a pure motive. Perhaps he was not truly repentant. I don't know. God even gave Cain a chance for a "do-over," but he was too angry and refused God's offer.

Adam and I didn't learn about the sacrifices until several days later. All we knew was that Cain had become angrier and more quick-tempered than he ever had been. Yet, he also seemed sadder, quieter. It was obvious he had something he couldn't get off his mind, but he didn't want to share whatever it was with us. This went on for several days, and both Adam and I tried to talk with him, but he just shut us out. It was Abel who finally told us about the sacrifices and what had happened.

When we learned about what was going on, we talked with Cain—or rather, we tried to talk with Cain. We thought by telling him that we knew the whole story, he would open up to us—share what he was feeling—and he would let us help him. Instead, he only seemed to get angrier and more withdrawn. Now he was angry not only at God but also at Abel because he felt Abel had tattled on him. I think he saw himself as a failure in God's sight, in Abel's sight, and now in our sight. We weren't sure what to do. We thought he would eventually come around, and things would go back to the way they had been. But things only got worse.

Everything came to a head one afternoon when the boys were walking out in the field together. We initially took that as a good sign—that Cain was coming around and the two of them were becoming friends again. Little did we know that we would never again see them, touch them, hug them, laugh with them, or talk with them. The last we saw them, they were together in the field.

We didn't know that people could die like that. We had seen animals die, and we had sacrificed animals ourselves, but we just didn't translate that to people. God had told us that our days would be numbered, but we really didn't understand what that meant yet! How could someone so young die? Why? And how could Cain have killed his own flesh and blood? What good could ever come of that? I had so many questions—questions that seemed to have no answers.

Ultimately Adam and I had to trust God. There was really nothing else we could do. Not only did we lose Abel that day, but we lost Cain as well. I also learned that day that the pain of childbirth isn't just at birth. It's with you the rest of your life as you watch your children make—and hopefully, learn from—their mistakes or when they're sick or injured. Your intense, painful love for them lasts a lifetime.

Life after that wasn't easy. I missed those two boys terribly. I felt lost. I had been a mother to those two for so long. But God was faithful. He never did desert us. He blessed Adam and me with many more children. The first son born to us after this tragic experience we named "Seth," which means "granted." God had granted us another son, and we were so happy. God truly can turn your sorrow into joy!

My friend, as I close this letter, I want to share with you some final thoughts. Be content. Lack of contentment was the underlying reason Adam and I were escorted out of the Garden of Eden. Learn to be happy with what God gives you—or doesn't give you.

And love those around you—especially children. Never take for granted the children God has entrusted to you. It doesn't matter if they're your own or someone else's—love them, nurture them, teach them about God. They can't get too much of your love and concern for them!

And lastly, but certainly no less important, be aware of how Satan tries to work in your life. For Adam and me, he first came disguised as a serpent. For Cain and Abel, I think he looked like competition. Always be on your guard. You can never be too careful. We lived the rest of our lives with the painful consequences of our actions that day in the Garden. But if we let them, those same consequences can teach us and remind us of lessons we've had to learn the hard way. Learn to listen to your gut feeling. Satan will come at you in different forms and in different ways. If you sense something is wrong, it probably is.

My precious friend, I apologize again for the length of this letter. But I thank you from the bottom of my heart for giving me the time and space to write my life story. I pray it has blessed you as much as it has me. In recounting my story, I realize that there were a lot of good times mixed in with the bad. We spend too much time focusing on all the bad stuff that happens and fail to give God thanks for the many blessings He gives us along the way. May God bless you, my dear friend, as you travel your own life's journey.

With much love,
Eve

Discussion/Reflection Questions

The following questions are designed to help you dig a bit more and think a little deeper. As the saying goes, "You will get out of this what you put into this." Don't short-change yourself. Take a few minutes to reflect on each of these questions and jot down your thoughts. If you are participating in a group study, consider sharing your discoveries with others in your small group.

You will notice reflection question #6 gives you the opportunity to write a return letter. This exercise is greatly encouraged because it will help you make a more personal connection.

1. Since Eve began life as an adult when she first encountered Satan, she didn't know or recognize what a lie was or how to argue with Satan. What are some childhood experiences you have gone through that helped prepare you for adulthood?

2. Eve justified her tasting of the fruit by thinking that it would be nice for God to have someone on His intellectual level to talk to. In what ways have you justified a sinful action? How have you tried to cover up sin?

3. In her letter, Eve mentions a couple of ways Satan disguised himself—in the form of a serpent and in the form of unhealthy competition. Under what kinds of disguises have you seen Satan come into your life or the lives of others?

4. Eve said that the lack of contentment is what ultimately caused Adam and her to sin and got them kicked out of the Garden of Eden. She urges us to be happy with our circumstances—to be happy with what God gives or doesn't give us. Do you consider yourself content? If not, why do you think contentment is such a hard thing to achieve?

5. Now that you've received and read your personal letter from Eve sharing with you her life's story, with which part can you most closely identify?

6. Now, it's your turn. Write a letter back to Eve. Write whatever you want. This is your personal letter to her. Some suggestions: Thank her for sharing her story. Tell her what sharing her story meant to you. Ask her questions. Let her know in what ways you can identify with her. Be imaginative!

NOTE: If you would like your letter to Eve to be considered for publication in a future book, you may do so by emailing a copy directly to: cheryllelliott@gmail.com.

You will be contacted personally if your letter is chosen to be represented in the book.

Please note that the deadline for receiving these letters is June 1, 2024 for printing in a book to be tentatively released the fall of 2024.

Abigail

One Tough Cookie

Abigail's story is found in 1 Samuel 25:2–42

My Dearest Friend,

It is my earnest prayer that God is blessing you. In your previous letter, you wrote that you felt like you didn't know a whole lot about me or my life. You also wrote that, based on what little you did know, you thought I was remarkable. Let me tell you upfront I never once considered myself or my life remarkable. I was much like you, living each day as it came and just doing the best I could. I know scripture says I was pretty and smart and had a great deal of wisdom, but I never felt that way at all about myself. I always felt I was average, dealing with a lot of the same insecurities most women battle. For the longest time, I felt I stood out only because I happened to marry into wealth. However, I didn't see that as a good thing because of the husband who came with it. If you'll allow me the time and space, let me share with you my story. Perhaps that will help you better understand who I was deep down.

You need to know I did not marry for love like you do today. During my lifetime, most marriages were either arranged by families or came about when a man took a liking to a woman he saw and declared her to be his. That's how I came to marry Nabal. When Nabal chose me, it wasn't anything I questioned because that's just the way it was. I didn't have a say in the matter. At first, I wasn't too upset because he was wealthy, and I knew I would be well taken care of, unlike a lot of women who struggled to keep their many children clothed and fed. I always thought that after we were married and spent more time together, I would gradually come to love Nabal. But that didn't happen. We were too different. As I reflect on it now, I think Nabal married me mostly because that was what was expected. Taking a wife just seemed to be another thing he could check off his list.

Back in my day, we attached a lot of meanings to names. And, for the most part, they seemed to fit our personalities as we got older. Nabal's name meant "fool," and he was every bit the fool in so many ways. He may have been rich, but he was a very disagreeable man. His foolishness caused me a great deal of hardship and heartache. In the past, I've said some not-so-nice things about him. And while they've all been true, it was not very kind of me to do that. I should have been better about keeping my opinions to myself. My mother always seemed to be telling me to "think before you speak." That's a lesson I struggled to learn. Let me just say that Nabal was dishonest, self-centered, and disrespectful of others. He tended to use people when it profited him. But he never returned the favor. Never.

As time went on, the more I came to know Nabal and who he really was, the more disillusioned I became. Since we had no children for me to take care of (and servants took care of me), my life became rather boring. I felt I was in a rut, and I didn't know how to get out of it. I longed for the day when a little excitement would come into my life—anything! I didn't care what. I just wanted a day when I could feel alive again. Useful. Needed. Loved. I hope you know what I mean.

Well, anyway, a day just like I had been longing for did happen. And although I didn't know it at the time, that one day turned out to be the beginning of a new life for me. I wrote earlier that Nabal tended to use people. That's how this day got its start. But first, let me back up a little and give you a brief background on what Nabal had done a few weeks earlier to lead up to this turn of events.

Although it was not his usual routine, Nabal was out in the fields with our herd and shepherds when trouble came. It happened that David and his men—this same David that we all knew was destined to become king one day—were out in nearby fields. When they learned what was happening, David and his men rushed to Nabal's aid. They protected him, his servant-shepherds, his herd—basically his entire wealth, which to Nabal meant everything. During the time David and his men protected Nabal's flocks, nothing Nabal owned was lost or stolen. Absolutely nothing! After they went their separate ways, Nabal returned home with everyone and everything he had left with, which probably would not have been the case if David hadn't been around and came to his rescue. I'm not sure Nabal ever thanked David for his help. But, if by some chance he did, I'm certain it was not heartfelt.

Well, fast-forward a few weeks, and now the sandal is on the other foot, so to speak. David is now in need of Nabal's help. Little did David know back then what kind of a man Nabal really was. But he was soon to find out. You would think that a man who had so much would be more gracious, more considerate, more generous. Oh, but not Nabal. He embarrassed me more times than I could count. Although he didn't know it at the time, what he did this particular day was the beginning of his undoing.

Since their encounter with Nabal, David and his 600 men had been living out in the nearby fields this whole time, keeping their distance from Saul who had vowed to kill David. Now they were running short of food, water, and other supplies. So, David sent messengers to Nabal to ask for help. Now, granted, David was asking for supplies for several hundred men. But Nabal was so wealthy that giving up that portion of provisions would hardly have been noticeable. It would have made only a small dent in what he had—a drop in the bucket. But instead of helping, Nabal was extremely rude to them. Here was the chance for Nabal to return a huge favor in a small way. Instead, he became hostile toward David's men. He even acted as if he didn't know who David was and all but accused the men of being renegade outlaws! Even the servant who came running to tell me what had happened was appalled. He said it was the worst treatment he had ever seen. He was terrified that the messengers would return with David and bring harm to Nabal and maybe even anyone or anything associated with him.

When the servant told me the details of what had happened, I was shocked. My heart sank clear down to my toes. Oh, how I wish I could have been there and talked to Nabal. Perhaps I could have talked some sense into him. But, since this happened during sheep-shearing time, there was a great celebration going on. While I was with the women, Nabal was entertaining the men, which meant there was food and drink in abundance. Nabal did nothing half-heartedly. The fact that there was already more than enough food and drink on hand would have been obvious to David's men and, therefore, made Nabal's actions even more atrocious. By the time the servant told me what had happened, I knew David's men had already left and were probably reporting back to David by now. So, I felt I had to act—and act fast!

I'd learned long ago that sometimes it was best to confront Nabal after the fact. If I had told him what I had planned, I'm sure he would have stopped me. So, I decided to take matters into my own hands. Thanks to the festivities already in full swing, I had ready access to all kinds of supplies. With the help of my servant girls, I gathered up 200 loaves of bread and a whole bunch of other things like wine, sheep, grain, and cakes—anything and everything I could think of. We loaded down donkeys and set out to find David and try to make amends.

The journey was slow-going because we were so loaded down—and on donkeys! So I had lots of time to think and pray. I was terrified of learning David's reaction to Nabal's slap in the face. Anyway, as I was riding my donkey down into a ravine (which, by the way, is easier said than done), I saw David and his men coming toward me. Even though I was looking for them, they nearly scared me to death because there were so many of them! And, by the way they were moving, you could certainly tell they were on a "mission." Here I was, slowly plodding along, trying to keep my balance on the donkey, and here they were, hundreds of them, marching straight toward me, armed to kill. They took up the entire path!

Without even thinking of getting out of their way or the possibility of being trampled, I took a deep breath, got off my donkey, and fell face down on the ground before David. I had already rehearsed in my mind what I would say to him at least a hundred times. I just hadn't expected to run into him so soon! I obviously underestimated how quickly David would respond to Nabal's dismissal. I thought I'd find David still out in the fields. Anyway, when I ran into him, even though it was on a narrow path leading down into a ravine, I just reacted by instinct and didn't think about the consequences. Covered from head to toe in dust and shaking uncontrollably, I was scared to even look at David. After all, I was Nabal's wife—the wife of the man with whom he was so infuriated! I had no idea how David would respond to me or to what I was about to say. But I had to at least try to beg his forgiveness.

So, before I even dared look at David, I begged him to let me take all the blame for Nabal's actions and to reconsider what he intended to do. Then, still trembling with fear, I began kind of inching my way up to my knees, all the time appealing to David's character and his relationship with the LORD. I knew David was a God-fearing man, so I started there, reminding him that revenge should be left to God and that he shouldn't pursue bloodshed to avenge himself—that he didn't want something like that hanging over his head when he became king. I was trusting God for what to say the entire time. At the end of my speech, I even asked David to remember me when he became king! Can you believe I was so bold as to ask such a thing? Me—a woman! A nobody! By the time David became king, he would have a whole lot more on his mind than trying to remember one woman! I was so embarrassed at blurting out such a remark that my face immediately turned beet red. To this day, I can't believe I said such a thing.

Anyway, to my great relief, David accepted my offering and my apology. Then he leaned forward and helped me to my feet and blessed me! I was stunned! He actually blessed me and thanked me for preventing him from taking matters into his own hands. He realized that seeking his own revenge would not have satisfied him—not really. Deep down, he knew that the peace he was looking for in this situation could only be found in God. That's also when David told me the extent of what he had planned—to kill not only Nabal but also all the men of our household by the next morning. How very thankful I was that I followed my gut feelings and sought David out to make amends. I thanked David profusely, gave him the provisions we had brought for him, and then parted company on much friendlier terms.

On the way back home, I knew I had to tell Nabal everything. So, just as I had done with David, I spent the time traveling rehearsing in my mind how I would go about doing that. I knew it wouldn't be easy and that he would be furious with me for what I had done. I prayed that he would see how it was the best thing to do, given the circumstances. I also knew I had to tell him immediately. There was no point in dragging it out, and, besides, he may have realized that I and some of my servant girls hadn't been around all day.

But when I got home, I found that he apparently hadn't missed me at all and instead was still in the middle of partying. By now, he had gotten very, very drunk. Seeing what was going on made me even madder about what he had done to David and his men! You know, what really ticked me off is that he probably spent more of his precious wealth on that drunken party of his than he would have if he'd just given the supplies to David, our future king, in the first place! Nabal's priorities were so messed up. Anyway, I now had to wait until the next day, after he was sober, to tell him. And let me tell you, the thought of confronting him and talking to him was almost as hard— if not harder—than the prospect of talking to David had been. After all, we women were taught—and expected—to revere our husbands. I had to be extremely careful how I went about telling Nabal so he wouldn't think I was being disrespectful. I wanted him to see that I only did what was in his best interest. Believe me, the entire time I was talking to him, I felt as if I was walking on eggshells. I knew that everything I said had to be worded just right.

But I also wanted him to realize the seriousness of what he had done and the danger he had put not only himself in but his innocent servants as well. My greatest desire was that he would begin to change. But, sadly, he didn't get that chance. God chose that exact moment to start seeking revenge on David's behalf. The moment Nabal fully realized the seriousness of the situation and how close he had come to losing it all, even his own life, his heart began giving him problems, and he died just ten days later. A lot of good his wealth did him then!

My life changed so much from that moment on. I can't say I mourned for Nabal a great deal. Keep in mind, we had a loveless marriage. I mostly just felt sorry for him. His life—and mine—could have been a whole lot better if only Nabal hadn't been so self-absorbed. You know, it's rather ironic but, as it turned out, it was shortly after Nabal died that I began to live! And I was probably the most surprised and shocked person of all. Let me tell you what happened.

Not long after Nabal's death, David's messengers once again came calling at my home. This time they specifically asked for me! David had heard about what had happened to Nabal, and he wasted no time in sending for me, asking me to marry him. Once more, I found myself face-down before David. I was so humbled that this man of God hadn't remembered my seemingly foolish "last words" but instead had found me wise and beautiful, even covered in dirt! Granted, it wasn't all romance, but it was wonderful compared to my life with Nabal. Remember, David and his men were still on the run from Saul at that time. So, my first days as David's wife were quite different from what I'd been accustomed to.

But life did settle down for me. And David did become king. And we did have children. At long last, my life felt complete. I was no longer lonely and bored, but I was busy and happy. What more could a girl ask?

Speaking of that, I urge you, my friend, to be careful what you ask for—God just might give it to you. He brought a whole lot more excitement into my life than I ever dreamed. Not that I regret any part of it or how things turned out, but it was rather stressful at the time.

Remember, too, that no matter how right you think you are, always be willing to stop and listen to the advice of others. David told me several times how thankful he was to have taken the time to hear me out that day on the path. What took just a few short minutes saved him from a lifetime of regret.

As I close this letter, I want to remind you that whatever you do, always trust God. When you're deeply concerned about someone or some situation, go to God. Talk to Him. Let Him guide your actions. Even when you're not sure of the outcome or the consequences, if you're trusting God completely, then you'll know everything will be okay in the end.

I love you, my dear friend. I'll see you when you get here!

Love,
Abigail

Discussion/Reflection Questions

The following questions are designed to help you dig a bit more and think a little deeper. As the saying goes, "You will get out of this what you put into this." Don't short-change yourself. Take a few minutes to reflect on each of these questions and jot down your thoughts. If you are participating in a group study, consider sharing your discoveries with others in your small group.

You will notice reflection question #6 gives you the opportunity to write a return letter. This exercise is greatly encouraged because it will help you make a more personal connection.

1. Nabal was so rich that giving up provisions for David would have hardly made a dent in his wealth. His entire life was consumed with things rather than the people around him. Even today, it often seems the richer people are, the stingier they tend to be. Why do you think that is?

2. When Abigail speaks to David, one of the first things she requests is that David put all the blame for Nabal's actions on her. How hard do you think that was for her? How would you have defended your husband had you been wearing Abigail's shoes?

3. Abigail was embarrassed at her closing remarks, asking David to remember her when he became successful and was crowned king. If Abigail had been trusting God for what to say, why do you think she thought her parting words were "off script"? Knowing the end of the story, were they? What do you think David thought about those last remarks?

4. Abigail urges us to be careful what we ask for—we just might get it. What examples in your life bear out the truth of that statement?

5. When we are wronged, our first reaction may not be like David's, which was to plan to murder the offender—at least, I hope not! How do you tend to react instead? How hard is it to listen to (and act on) advice that is the opposite of what you want to hear?

6. Now, it's your turn. Write a letter back to Abigail. Write whatever you want. This is your personal letter to her. Some suggestions: Thank her for sharing her story. Tell her what sharing her story meant to you. Ask her questions. Let her know in what ways you can identify with her. Be imaginative!

NOTE: If you would like your letter to Abigail to be considered for publication in a future book, you may do so by emailing a copy directly to: cheryllelliott@gmail.com.

You will be contacted personally if your letter is chosen to be represented in the book.

Please note that the deadline for receiving these letters is June 1, 2024 for printing in a book to be tentatively released the fall of 2024.

Mrs. Manoah

(a.k.a. Samson's Mom)

Mrs. Manoah's story is found in Judges 13:1–16:31

My Dearest Friend,

I pray that you continue to do well and are happily serving God in the way He has called you. I wanted to write this letter to share with you my life's story. I won't go into detail, but there are some things about my life that I feel are important for you to know.

I always saw myself as someone who lived in the background. I wasn't the kind of person who sought out the spotlight. And I was okay with that. You know, I didn't always think I had a story to tell—at least not a very exciting or memorable story—and certainly not a story of great significance. It wasn't until a friend pointed out to me that, of all the hundreds of thousands of women who have ever lived, I am one of a very few who had an angel come and visit her. And that happened twice! That's perhaps the most amazing part of my life's story I want to share.

You may or may not know this, but my husband, Manoah, and I had been married for quite some time and had not been able to have children. From the time I was a little girl, that's all I ever wanted—marriage and children. Back in my day, that's about the only thing that made any woman's life of value—her ability to have children, and lots of them! My husband and I both wanted a child in the worst way. I had long since given up on having a house full of children. Let's face it: we were getting old, and at that point in our lives, I would have been happy to have even one child, boy or girl. I just wanted a baby to hold in my arms.

Then one day, the strangest thing happened. Out of the clear blue, this man appeared in front of me and told me I was barren and childless. How odd. My first thought was anything but gracious. I wanted to know who he was and why he was "rubbing salt in my wound." I already knew I didn't have any children. I'll admit I was already feeling down in the dumps and out of sorts that day. Nothing seemed to be going right. Then, to be reminded of this awful fact by a stranger no less made my already bad mood even worse. It took all I had not to burst into tears. Even though I had not said a word, evidently, this stranger could see how distraught I was because he wasted no time in blurting out that I would become pregnant and give birth to a son. I was in such shock I had to pinch myself! Did I hear what I thought I heard? I literally froze in my tracks. Eyes wide and mouth hanging open, I just stood there, dumbfounded. And what's perhaps even more amazing is that, for whatever reason, I believed him! Why I don't know. Maybe it was his mannerism or the matter-of-fact way in which he said it, but I had absolutely no doubt he knew something I didn't. I believed him instantly! In retrospect, this was quite amazing for me because I wasn't usually a gullible person—especially with strangers regarding serious issues. And, believe me, having a child was a serious issue! What's more, he then told me another strange thing—that I immediately needed to go on a strict diet! At first, I was a bit insulted by this declaration. It wasn't until he explained how important the diet would be to my baby and the reasoning behind it that I understood.

This man told me that the diet was because my son— my *son*, mind you—was going to be a very special man. He said that my son would be a Nazirite, which was the reason for my need to start this strict diet. I'm not sure if you know what a Nazirite was, but, in a nutshell, it was a person who made a vow to be set aside for God's service. Part of that vow involved a list of dietary restrictions. Sometimes a Nazirite vow was temporary—only for a certain period of time. And sometimes, people made the vow intending it to be for the rest of their lives. In our case—our son's case—it was literally for life, which is why I was put on this special diet even before I conceived.

Being under the same restrictions as the Nazarite vow meant that I was not to drink any wine, other fermented drink of any kind, have anything from the grapevine, or eat anything unclean. This way, from the very second of the beginning of my son's life in the womb to his death, he was a Nazirite. There was never a time in his life that he wasn't under the special vow. Another requirement of the Nazirite vow he had to abide by was to never, ever, cut his hair. While this may sound strange to you, it was customary in my day for people who were set aside as Nazirites to not cut their hair during the entire period of their vow. The only unusual thing in my son's case was that the Nazirite vow was placed *upon* him instead of it being a voluntary commitment on his part. And his vow was for the duration of his life, not the shorter, designated period as was the custom. Oh, dear friend, I just realized the lengthy tangent I took. I am so sorry. Let me get back to my life's story.

Well, as quickly as this man of God appeared, he disappeared! All the time he was in front of me, I had not been able to utter one word! I have no idea how long I stood there in shock afterward, trying to process everything I had just seen and heard. But finally, it dawned on me that I needed to tell Manoah. I was so excited and couldn't wait to tell him about the baby—especially since I had been told the baby was going to be a boy. I wasn't sure how Manoah would react to my story, but I knew he would be so thrilled at even the thought that he was going to have a son! It wasn't until I started hearing the words come out of my mouth that I realized how absurd my story sounded. And I realized that I had a lot of unanswered questions.

For starters, I didn't know the first thing about the man who had talked to me. I didn't know his name or where he came from—nothing! Then there was the problem of how to describe him. I thought he must have been a man of God, maybe even an angel, but I wasn't sure at the time. After all, I'd never, ever had an angel come to me before—and really never expected to. So, when it came to describing him, I found myself at a loss for words. I finally could only come up with one word to sum up his appearance—*awesome*. Very awesome, indeed.

Another big question I had was whether people—Manoah included—would think I had been dreaming or, worse yet, had lost my mind. After all, we were living in a time when the nation of Israel as a body wasn't exactly obeying God as it should. And because of that, God had allowed us to become subjected to the Philistines. Evil was becoming increasingly prevalent every day. I guess I thought there was a chance Manoah wouldn't believe me—after all, God was very unhappy with the Israelite nation, so why would He bother with one couple who was struggling to have a baby? How important could that be to God when there was so much else going on?

But would you believe that Manoah didn't bat an eye? Instead, he took my hands and helped me to my knees. Then Manoah began praying. He didn't doubt or question me at all—not for a second. He believed me immediately, and his first reaction was to pray! Unlike a lot of Israel at the time, Manoah was a God-fearing man, and our praying together was not all that unusual. But this time, I thought Manoah was especially bold and daring in his request. It surprised me when Manoah asked for the man of God to be sent back to us so he could tell us how to "rear" our son. I must admit that I wasn't at all sure this prayer of his would ever be answered! Can you imagine? I mean, in all honesty, with his first visit, we'd already been blessed beyond what most people ever experienced. After all, it wasn't every day people had a man of God appear to them.

But you know what? The man of God did return—just not quite as we expected. I guess we both assumed that if he came back (and that was a big *if*, mind you), it would be to either Manoah or to the two of us together. Instead, he appeared to me while I was out in the field all by myself—again! My first thought was, once more, not so gracious. It's a good thing my mom taught me the importance of thinking before speaking. This time I wondered, *Why do you keep popping up when I'm all by myself? Couldn't you at least come when Manoah's around?* But he didn't. Here he was, and here I was, and here Manoah wasn't. I knew Manoah would be devastated to miss this man yet again. So, I pleaded with him to stay put and not go anywhere.

I asked him if he would wait while I ran to get Manoah. I realize now that the smarter thing would have been to ask the man to walk back to the house with me. Oh, well.

Anyway, I ran as quickly as I could to get Manoah. By the time the two of us got back to the field where I had left the man, we were both quite out of breath—especially me. After all, in one day, I'd already run the length of this field more times than I cared to count! So, between gasps for air, I introduced Manoah to the man who had appeared to me. This man of God was so patient with Manoah. He could tell that Manoah wanted to say something, but Manoah was stumbling all over his words. It seemed the harder Manoah tried to talk, the more tongue-tied he became. To his credit, the man just patiently stood there, smiling and waiting.

When Manoah finally found his words, do you know what he asked him? He asked the man if he was the one who had talked to me. I couldn't believe it! After all, I had just introduced him as such. Here I was, doubled over, hands on my knees, and still trying to catch my breath. When Manoah asked that, I sighed, gave him a sideways glance, and thought, *You have got to be kidding! I cannot believe what you just said. You mean to tell me we came running all this way for you to ask him that?* After all, we were in the middle of a field, and he was the only other man around! Who else did he think this guy could possibly be?

Anyway, do you know what the man of God did? He smiled at Manoah and said, "I am." That's all he said! There was this uncomfortably long pause—you know, the kind where the silence is nearly deafening. Then, finally, Manoah's brain and tongue began to function simultaneously, and he asked the man what he intended to ask in the first place, which was for more instruction on how we are to bring up our son. Actually, he asked it much more eloquently than that. My dear husband said something like, "When your words are fulfilled, what is to be the rule that governs the boy's life and work?" That's *not* exactly how I would have worded it. And that's not how Manoah had prayed earlier, nor was it how Manoah usually talked. But I guess, in this man's presence, Manoah was a bit uncomfortable and wanted to sound more dignified than either of us looked at that moment!

But you know what struck me about this man of God? He didn't seem to notice our appearance, what we said, or how we said it. Instead, he just talked to us in a manner that was so soothing, so comforting. He told Manoah that I must do all he had already told me to do. Although we were a bit disappointed, the man of God—an angel, as we were soon to learn—was so reassuring in his voice and the way he acted that somehow, even though he didn't say it in words, we knew that we would know what to do when the time came.

Manoah shook his head in understanding and asked if he would let us prepare a goat and feed him. But the man wouldn't hear of it. Instead, he told us that, if we wanted to, we could offer a burnt offering to the LORD. So that's what we set out to do. Meanwhile, Manoah asked the man what his name was so we would know to whom to give credit when everything came true. But he wouldn't tell us. Instead, he said that it was "beyond understanding." That was very puzzling, but we didn't pursue it any further. Somehow, we didn't feel the need.

So, we finished gathering supplies for the burnt offering (the goat and some grain) and sacrificed it on a rock to the LORD. Then—oh, you are not going to believe what happened next! It's hard for me to believe even to this day—and I was standing right there watching with my own two eyes! Without warning, this huge flame blazed up from the altar and went straight toward heaven! And this man, this angel of the LORD, ascended in the flame. It was at that moment we knew without a doubt that the man had, indeed, been sent by God.

Manoah and I had two very different reactions to this realization. Manoah went straight into what I consider panic mode. He began yelling, "We're doomed! We've just seen God! Now we're going to die!" I couldn't believe how Manoah was acting. It wasn't the reaction I expected from him. He was usually so calm, cool, and collected. But, in all fairness to Manoah, death was usually the result for anyone who physically saw God. So, while his reaction seemed extreme, I could understand it.

I didn't feel anything like Manoah—that we were doomed to die, that is. I felt just the opposite—that I now had more life than ever before. After all, when you stop to think about it, why would the LORD do all this and tell us all this just to kill us? It just didn't make sense.

Well, as it turned out, I was right. We didn't die (at least not until many, many years later), and I did become pregnant. Several months later, I gave birth to a very precious baby boy whom we named Samson. And, from that moment on, we became known as Samson's mom and dad. I'm sure you've probably heard about him. He's a whole lot more famous than Manoah and I combined. Anyway, from that point on, our whole lives became wrapped up in the life of that young man.

Being Samson's mother was hard. Manoah and I had done the best we knew how in rearing him. Yet, he struggled a lot. And it hurt like crazy to see him make his mistakes. All we could do was sit back and watch him struggle. Keep in mind that Israel was still going through a rebellious time of spiritual and moral decay. And there were very few godly examples for Samson to follow. Manoah and I had tried to live as we should, and we did our best to instill in him the importance of not only following the outward appearances in fulfilling the Nazirite vow but also striving for inner holiness. We wanted him to understand the importance of surrendering his will to God. That's one area he struggled so much with—his will vs. God's will.

But in the end, God was able to accomplish His will through Samson despite his weaknesses or any parenting mistakes Manoah or I made along the way. And just before his death, Samson reconnected with God and turned back to fully obeying Him. Once Samson finally prayed for God's strength, the two of them together managed to kill more Philistines in one moment than Samson had throughout his entire lifetime. Samson's life was proof that it's never too late to surrender and be obedient to God.

My dear friend, I can't stress enough how important it is to be obedient to God. Do what God is telling you to do, whether you understand it now or not. And if you're not sure what you're supposed to do, ask Him! Then don't forget to stop and listen. He'll tell you! And if you're playing the "battle of wills" game with God, give up, surrender, and go ahead and let Him win—He's going to anyway, you know. So, save yourself some frustration and heartache and do what He wants you to do.

There is one last thing I want to tell you. I know there have been occasions when you have beaten yourself up because of your own wayward child. Stop. If you did the best you knew to do in bringing him or her up, turn them completely over to God. You are not responsible for their poor choices, just as your parents are not responsible for any of yours. Trust God. He loves your child as much as you do—more actually! He has a plan for the life of that child of yours, and He can work His plan despite any side roads he or she wanders along. Even through their mistakes—or yours—God is able to work. Just continue to set a good example and pray, pray, pray. God can turn their life around regardless of how dismal it may look to you right now.

I love you, my friend, and I pray the best for you and your family.

Yours always,
"Samson's mom"

Discussion/Reflection Questions

The following questions are designed to help you dig a bit more and think a little deeper. As the saying goes, "You will get out of this what you put into this." Don't short-change yourself. Take a few minutes to reflect on each of these questions and jot down your thoughts. If you are participating in a group study, consider sharing your discoveries with others in your small group.

You will notice reflection question #6 gives you the opportunity to write a return letter. This exercise is greatly encouraged because it will help you make a more personal connection.

1. Mrs. Manoah seemed shocked that God would take the time or make the effort to bother with her problems and concerns. Can you think of a time when God surprised you by answering a prayer that, at the time, seemed so trivial you were almost ashamed to mention it to God?

2. When Mrs. Manoah told her husband about the man's visit and what he had told her, Manoah immediately believed her. Why do you think that was?

3. Even though he shared no new information, the

angel came back to Mrs. Manoah a second time. Why do you think he did that? And why do you think he chose to show up again when Mrs. Manoah was alone, even though he apparently was willing to talk to Manoah as well?

4.   In the presence of the angel, Manoah found himself speaking more formally than normal. We often hear that in our own churches today. Why do you think people tend to speak "fancier" when they're praying in public? Is it wrong?

5.   Pretend there is a board game called "Battle of Wills." The starting point is called "Your Will," and the finish line is "God's Will." There are fifty stepping-stones between. Think about which stone you would say you're on. What experiences have you gone through in your life that have helped to move you along the path to a hundred percent surrender and full obedience to God's will for your life? How can you be certain you know what God's will is for you?

6.   Now, it's your turn. Write a letter back to Mrs. Manoah. Write whatever you want. This is your personal letter to Samson's mom. Some suggestions: Thank her for sharing her story. Tell her what sharing her story meant to

you. Ask her questions. Let her know in what ways you can identify with her. Be imaginative!

NOTE: If you would like your letter to Mrs. Manoah to be considered for publication in a future book, you may do so by emailing a copy directly to: cheryllelliott@gmail. com.

You will be contacted personally if your letter is chosen to be represented in the book.

Please note that the deadline for receiving these letters is June 1, 2024 for printing in a book to be tentatively released the fall of 2024.

Mrs. Lot

Ignored God's Warning

Mrs. Lot's story is found in Genesis 11:27–19:26

My Dearest Friend,

I sincerely pray that you are being blessed by God more than you could ever imagine. Our God is awesome and loves us more than we realize. Without a doubt, I know that now. But that wasn't always the case. I made some big mistakes during my lifetime, but nothing of what I did negated God's love for me. I'm writing because I want to share with you my story, in my words.

Let me give you a little bit of background on the man I came to marry. Lot had a rough childhood. His mother died giving birth to him and his father, Haran, died not too many years later. So, Lot went to live with his grandfather, Terah, who decided to move his family from Ur of the Chaldeans (where Lot had grown up) to Canaan. However, it wasn't too long into their journey that they had to stop because Terah became extremely sick. It was only a few days later that he also passed away. This left Lot orphaned yet again. Thankfully Lot's uncle and aunt, Abram and Sarai, took him in. A few years later, Lot and I met, married, and began accumulating our own possessions—servants, sheep, livestock—you know, your normal stuff.

When Lot and I were first married, we were young. Very young. And even though we were starting our own separate household, we still lived with Abram and Sarai—the only family Lot had left. Then, one day, Uncle Abram decided to go ahead and move his family on to Canaan to fulfill his father's dream. Because we were young, the thought of travel intrigued us, so we decided to move as well. The fact that we were young worked in our favor. But, as we got older, not so much. We did a lot of traveling in our early years together. Not only was it romantic traveling to new places, it was also exciting to meet new people. As a people person, I loved that. But eventually, all the traveling became something I began to dread. All the packing and moving got to be overwhelming—especially as we accumulated more and more stuff. After a while, all the living out of a suitcase, so to speak, really got to be old. Yet, every time Uncle Abram and Aunt Sarai pulled up stakes, we did as well. We never really discussed whether we would go with them; it was just kind of a given. Besides, Uncle Abram and Aunt Sarai didn't have any children of their own at the time, so they had kind of adopted Lot and me as their children. That was another reason to move—to stay close to them. So, we all traveled together to Canaan and eventually settled near a town called Bethel. That's where our two daughters were born. I loved the feeling of being settled.

But then a famine happened in our area, and food became scarce—not only for us but for feeding our livestock as well. So, Uncle Abram decided it was time to move on again, this time to Egypt. That move was especially hard on me because, by this time, I had to keep track of two curious toddlers as we traveled. We had been in Egypt only a short time when Uncle Abram and Egypt's Pharaoh had a "difference of opinion" about Aunt Sarai. And, before we knew it, we found ourselves being promptly escorted out of the country—by armed guards, nonetheless! I had never been so embarrassed in my life. It seemed everyone was looking and pointing at us as we scampered about packing up our things and loading the donkeys!

Finally, we were far enough away that the armed escorts returned to Egypt while we, not knowing where else to go, headed back to Bethel. We knew life would still be hard because the land was only just beginning to recover from the serious drought. The traveling was so hard on the girls. And Uncle Abram and Aunt Sarai weren't getting any younger either, you know! All the traveling was taking a toll on everyone. But we finally made it back to Bethel, and I began unpacking—again!

When we returned, there was some talk among the locals (as well as our own servants and shepherds) regarding what we had done. Some think Uncle Abram jumped the gun and ran off to Egypt too quickly, not trusting God to take care of us. But no one could be sure what would have happened had we stayed. After all, the famine had been extremely harsh. Bottom line, we all do what we think is best at the time we are faced with any uncertain situation.

Anyway, we—Lot and I—trusted Uncle Abram. He was always trying to do what God wanted and was always listening for the LORD's voice to guide him. To finally get back home was all I really cared about. I had never been so happy to get unpacked and settled in my life!

The upside I could see during all of this is that we did prosper abundantly along the way. So, it wasn't all a waste! Both Uncle Abram and Lot became very wealthy during the months we were gone, with more sheep, cattle, servants, silver, gold—lots of things. But you know, it was actually because of that wealth that we ended up moving yet again!

Remember when I said that the land had just gone through a very severe famine? Well, while the water and crops were beginning to get back to normal, they still had a long way to go. Finding enough water and grain to take care of all the livestock that belonged to both Uncle Abram and Lot became a full-time, frustrating job for our herdsmen.

One day Uncle Abram asked Lot to take a walk with him. This wasn't too unusual because they did have more of a father-son relationship. But, while they were walking along, Lot noticed that something seemed to be bothering

Uncle Abram. Lot thought perhaps he wasn't feeling well. Uncle Abram assured him he was okay and then began talking about the overcrowded situation. Lot agreed. Lot and I had already talked about the problem and knew something needed to be done, but we didn't know what. And, being the younger of the two, Lot didn't feel that it was his place to suggest a new arrangement. But it became obvious this had been weighing heavily on Uncle Abram's mind. When Lot asked him what he thought the solution was, Uncle Abram suggested we split up and go our separate ways. He then pointed out the fact that the land to the East, known as the Jordan Valley, was fertile and well-watered. He suggested that one of them move there with all their possessions, household servants, and shepherds while the other remain in Canaan.

At first, Lot wasn't too keen on that idea at all. He just knew Uncle Abram would want to go where the land was better and life would be easier. And, being the senior member of the family, it certainly was his right to choose the best spot. But that's not what Uncle Abram suggested at all. Instead, he looked Lot square in the eyes and told *him* to choose. At first, I think Lot thought it was a trick. On the one hand, you would have plenty of water and food for your family, livestock, and servants. On the other hand, life would be more of a struggle. But Lot knew his Uncle

Abram loved him and wanted him to be happy. So, it didn't take Lot too long to say, "I'll take the Jordan Valley."

This, of course, meant yet another move, which I was not thrilled about. The traveling that once was so glamorous and romantic was now a chore! Then, Lot pointed out all the advantages. When he mentioned living near a big city, that cinched it for me. Finally, this girl could do some major shopping! And, moving to the city would also allow me to have more friends and perhaps even host parties— something I hadn't been able to do. It meant we could now get a more permanent home than the tent we had been lugging around, and I wouldn't have to be ashamed to have people over anymore. Just think…an actual house, with a doorway and windows and everything! It was like a dream come true!

I was so excited. I began packing immediately. And I packed endlessly until we were all ready. It seemed my energy level skyrocketed almost overnight. I couldn't wait to get settled into our new home and get on with the life I'd always dreamed.

Apart from the sadness of leaving, I was also concerned about Aunt Sarai, who seemed a bit disappointed. I think she would have liked to have had a bit easier time of it, too. But, at the same time, she was also happy for us. Both she and Uncle Abram loved Lot like a son. More than anything, they wanted Lot to be happy and successful. I'm sure Aunt Sarai understood my excitement. However, when I was around her, I did try to tone things down a bit, but it was so hard!

Despite all my exhilaration, as moving day dawned, I found myself a bit apprehensive. There were a hundred questions that popped up in my head at the last minute. After all, we had been country folks for a long time. *What if we didn't fit in? What if they didn't like us? What if the girls couldn't find playmates? What if I couldn't find a best friend?* There were so many unknowns. But you know, it didn't take long at all for us to fit right in. Granted, our wealth probably didn't hurt any. People always seem to be drawn to money and possessions. Deep down, I knew that some of my "friends" were only spending time with me because of my status as a wealthy woman. But you know, I really didn't care. I was more interested in the prestige I had: a nice big house, a handsome husband, two beautiful daughters, and lots of friends. I wanted everyone to like me. And I did everything I could to see that they did.

I made it my goal to have one of the largest, nicest homes around. I entertained a lot. I made sure the girls and I always had the latest colorful fashions and tons of jewelry. Basically, I flaunted our wealth in every way possible. And Lot, well, I made sure he was always dressed in his finest and that he mingled as much as he could with the other men of Sodom—especially the important men.

My life had taken a 180-degree turn. I'll admit that, at first, I was a bit uncomfortable. After all, if people found out, what would they think of our previous near-nomadic lifestyle? If, instead of adoring me and envying me, would they pity me? It was hard early on. To blend in, we kept secret so many things from our past. But as time passed, the memories passed as well. It got easier—too easy, in fact.

Before I knew it, we were living the lie. It was almost as if the Lot and Mrs. Lot we used to be no longer existed, and we were now the new and improved, rich man Lot and his wife who lived in the wealthiest suburb of Sodom. We had become so entangled in this lifestyle that the new "us" no longer prayed or worshipped the LORD as we should have. In fact, the new "us" hardly gave the LORD a thought at all until...well, until that one fateful evening several years later.

This particular evening, Lot met a couple of men at the city gate and invited them home. Lot and I had become well-known for our hospitality, so it wasn't unusual for Lot to bring people home for supper. Shortly after we had finished eating, we began to hear quite a commotion at the front door. When Lot went to find out what was going on, he was appalled! Some men in town were demanding that Lot turn the two men over to them. We had lived in Sodom long enough by now to know they were up to no good, so Lot refused. But they insisted. Finally, they lunged at Lot. When they did, the two men—angels, as we later learned—reached out, pulled Lot back inside, and quickly bolted the door. They also caused the men outside to become blind, so they couldn't see to break in or hurt us.

The girls and I were terrified! Then the angels told us why they were there—that the city had become so sinful and corrupt and so detestable to the LORD that He was going to destroy it. I was so confused at the time. I couldn't seem to think clearly and didn't quite understand. As I began to process what the two men said, I began to have this sadness overwhelm me. We had become friends with so many people in this town. My best friend lived just down the street, our daughters were engaged, and the house was finally just as I dreamed. Life was going so well. But deep down, Lot and I knew things weren't right. We knew we had strayed from the LORD. But we liked our new, comfortable lifestyle. Even though we knew we were wrong, we liked it. We were happy. However, I don't think we realized just how numb we had become to sin. My dear friend, does that make any sense? We had gradually become tolerant and accepting of what we knew to be *sin*. That's so easy to do when that is all that's around you. Up until the men (angels) pointed that out, we hadn't realized that we were the only ones who still had an ounce of morality left. We had been told that God would save the city if ten innocent people could be found. Do you know how many God found? Four! In the big city of Sodom, only four: Lot, me, and our two daughters. That's all! Not even our future sons-in-law believed. And you know, come to think about it, I'm not so sure how "innocent" the four of us were. We certainly had strayed from what we knew was right. But the LORD was gracious and merciful to us.

Well, after things finally settled down that evening, the men told us to get some rest because the next day we would need to leave before the city was destroyed. Yeah, right! Who could rest with all this about to happen? I think I must have been in a state of shock because I couldn't seem to do anything except walk through the house and look at everything. We had been told not to take anything with us except the clothes on our backs. So, I didn't need to pack this time. Instead, I spent the night pacing the floor, crying, feeling sorry for myself, fingering our possessions one last time, and worrying about the future.

The girls were so concerned about their fiancés that finally Lot went out to try to convince them to leave with us as well. But they wouldn't. They didn't even believe

Lot—they thought he was joking. Little did they know
that Lot had never been more serious about anything in his
life! So, Lot finally gave up, came back home, and broke
the news to the girls. They were devastated. After all, they
were both so young and impressionable when we first
moved to Sodom that they had become acclimated to the
lifestyle even more than Lot or I. Now, to lose their dreams
of marriage and children only compounded their loss. It
was an impossibly long night for all of us.

At dawn the next morning, the angels began yelling at
us—telling us to hurry up and get out—to leave the city
immediately! But we couldn't seem to move—not one of
us! Our feet seemed glued to the floor. Finally, the angels
took us by the hands and literally dragged us out of the
city. At the same time, they were telling us to run for our
lives—to run and not look back. The LORD was so merciful
to reach out and save us as He did. If it hadn't been for the
angels, I'm not sure what would have happened. Finally,
it was as if everything clicked—our brains, our feet—
everything! And we began to run as hard and as fast as we
could.

That's when the sky began to turn brilliant shades of
red, orange, yellow, and white. And we began to hear all
kinds of sounds—buildings crumbling, people screaming.
It was horrible. Now Lot was the one who was yelling,

"Run, run! Don't look back. Just keep running. Faster, faster!" I heard him, and I wanted to keep running. And I tried so hard not to look back. Honestly, I did. But I couldn't resist.

Yes, I know I shouldn't have. But have you ever had one of those moments when you knew you shouldn't do something, and everything in and around you told you not to? But you did it anyway? That's what was going on. I just wanted to see my home one last time. I was so fearful of what the future would hold. I didn't know where we were headed or what we were going to do. How could we start all over with only the clothes on our backs? I just couldn't seem to let go of the past. I thought one little glance wouldn't hurt. I didn't plan to stare—or even to look, for that matter. It was just a peek. One quick, short, little peek. But that's all it took. My life as I knew it on earth ended with that one little, seemingly harmless glance.

Precious friend, it is my prayer you learn from some of my many mistakes. And, believe me, I made a lot of them! Never let wealth lure you away from God. Lot and I were not spiritually mature enough to manage our wealth or a city such as Sodom—not many people are.

Also, beware of drowning out God's voice with other things. I realized too late that's exactly what I had been doing under the disguise of "entertaining." As long as I had people around or filled my days with "busyness," I didn't have to hear—or listen to—the still, small voice inside of me. With everything in me, I urge you to listen to God. Whatever He tells you to do—do it. Be obedient. If He tells you to move, move! If He tells you not to look, don't! I was disobedient and paid for it with my life. Don't you go and do the same. Learn from my mistakes.

Another mistake I must confess is being reluctant to let go of the past. If God is leading (or pushing) you in a new direction, don't let your fear of the future stop you as it did me. Keep your eyes focused on God and the direction He is leading you. Once you do that, you can be confident everything will work out.

My friend, thank you for taking the time to read my story. Without a doubt, my life had its share of ups and downs. But I can honestly write this: it didn't matter if I was going through rough stuff or smooth sailing. God was with me. He's just like that. It's my final prayer that you would recognize God's grace, mercy, and love. And that you would readily ask for—and receive—God's forgiveness.

Your forever girlfriend,
Mrs. Lot

Discussion/Reflection Questions

The following questions are designed to help you dig a bit more and think a little deeper. As the saying goes, "You will get out of this what you put into this." Don't short-change yourself. Take a few minutes to reflect on each of these questions and jot down your thoughts. If you are participating in a group study, consider sharing your discoveries with others in your small group.

You will notice reflection question #6 gives you the opportunity to write a return letter. This exercise is greatly encouraged because it will help you make a more personal connection.

1. Lot and his wife seemed to justify their tolerance of sin as a small price to pay in order to live the affluent lifestyle they desired. Besides the question of what constitutes a family, what are some other issues in which Christians today are being slowly desensitized and becoming more tolerant of sin?

2. Mrs. Lot gave in to the urge to take one last peek at Sodom. Why do you think she found this command to not look back so hard? If God were to ask you to move on to something else in your life, how hard would it be for you

to let go of the past? Can you hold on to pieces of your old life as you move forward with God? Why or why not?

3. Mrs. Lot insinuated that even though their trip to Egypt seemed like a waste of time and energy to us, maybe there was a purpose for it that they weren't aware of at the time. Have you ever had something similar happen to you—for which you didn't (or maybe still don't) fully understand the reason?

4. Often, we hear people ask God for a direct sign to confirm what He wants them to do. Mrs. Lot got that. She literally had an angel's hand pulling her away from Sodom and leading her to her future. Still, she looked back. Have you ever received a clear sign from God about something? If so, what was it, and how hesitant were you to follow through?

5. Too often, we see only the positive side of things, ignoring the negatives. If you had the chance to change your life overnight and become a millionaire, would you? Why or why not? How much of a factor is age? Do you think the older a person is, the better they are able to manage wealth—sudden or not? Why or why not?

6. Now, it's your turn. Write a letter back to Mrs. Lot. Write whatever you want. This is your personal letter to her. Some suggestions: Thank her for sharing her story. Tell her what sharing her story meant to you. Ask her questions. Let her know in what ways you can identify with her. Be imaginative!

NOTE: If you would like your letter to Mrs. Lot to be considered for publication in a future book, you may do so by emailing a copy directly to: cheryllelliott@gmail.com.

You will be contacted personally if your letter is chosen to be represented in the book.

Please note that the deadline for receiving these letters is June 1, 2024 for printing in a book to be tentatively released the fall of 2024.

Hannah

Remarkable Trust

Hannah's story is found in 1 Samuel 1:1–2:21

My Dearest Friend,

Thank you for your letter. What an honor it is to share my story with you. Too often, I think, women feel their lives are nothing special, and they have no testimony to share with others. But that's not the case at all. If you have experienced the highs and lows of living on earth, then you have a testimony that needs to be told.

I grew up in an average home and had a relatively normal childhood. Like all young girls, I often dreamed of marriage and children. After all, taking care of a husband, home, and children was pretty much all we girls were trained to do. My mother spent hours teaching me everything she knew about cooking, sewing, and caring for a home and a family. The older I got, the more eager I became to get married, settle down, and start having babies to care for of my own. The day I married Elkanah was the happiest day of my life. I was finally able to start putting everything I had learned into practice.

Elkanah and I first met on one of my family's trips to Shiloh. He was traveling with his family, and I was traveling with mine. Our caravans happened onto the same path at about the same time. It was love at first sight. I was one of the lucky ones. In the culture I grew up in, too many times, a man and woman didn't necessarily marry for love. Sometimes marriages were arranged. Sometimes marriages came about when a man became infatuated with a woman he saw. But Elkanah and I knew we had special feelings for one another early on. I thought he was perhaps the most handsome man I had ever seen. And I was so comfortable talking with him. It was as if I had known him my entire life!

When we met, our families were both headed to Shiloh to attend a religious festival. It was required that all Israelite men attend these festivals, which happened several times a year. The men didn't always take their families along with them for the journey. But this festival was one of special significance for Israel as a whole. It was a time set aside for the entire Israelite nation to offer sacrifices at the temple and offer praises to the LORD. So, it wasn't uncommon for men to take their entire families along so they could celebrate as well. And that's where both our families were headed. It's possible that Elkanah and I had run into each other on earlier trips to Shiloh—we just hadn't "seen" each other, if you know what I mean! With love, it's all in the timing and two hearts being right for each other. So, not long after this trip, Elkanah and I married. And I could not have been happier.

But after being married for quite some time, we still had no children. Since having children was of utmost importance, we agreed that Elkanah should also marry a girl named Peninnah, or "Ninnah," as we nicknamed her. The only reason they married was so Elkanah could have children to carry on his family's name. It's kind of ironic: I had Elkanah's love but not his children. Ninnah had his children but not his love.

At first, I was okay with this arrangement. Now, don't get me wrong—it hurt like crazy. But I understood. It was so important to Elkanah that he had children. And it had become obvious that I would not be able to give him the son he wanted. But I knew he loved me. And I loved him so much. I wanted this for him as much as he wanted it for himself. It wasn't until later—several years later, in fact— that I began to have serious doubts about the arrangement.

By this time, Ninnah had borne Elkanah child after child after child—both sons and daughters. There seemed to be no end to her having children. Yet, during all that time, I still hadn't had any—not one! Oh, how I prayed and prayed. All I wanted was a child—just one child! It was especially difficult when we went to Shiloh each year for our worship time. It was then that I really battled with my emotions. I struggled so much with feeling as if God wasn't listening to me, that He didn't love me enough to grant me my one heart's desire. But, deep down, I knew better than that!

My parents had brought me up to realize that God

doesn't always give us what we ask for—or beg for, for that matter. But He would always give us exactly what we needed when we needed it. For me, I felt abandoned by God the most on our yearly trips to Shiloh. This was supposed to be a time of special worship and praise to God. But, oh, how I struggled. And Ninnah didn't help matters any. Every year Ninnah would line up all her children before Elkanah so he could give them—and Ninnah herself—their portion of meat for the sacrifice. When that time came, it was so obvious what I didn't have—children. Every year I stood there alone. And there she stood, with all her children, gloating over the many times the LORD had blessed her. Then she would begin taunting me about how I was not being blessed, insinuating that I was barren because the LORD God had put a curse on me.

I knew that I wasn't under a curse. But, in my day, that's what a lot of people thought. We all knew what a blessing children were. So, many people assumed that if you didn't have a child, it was because you had done something bad, and the LORD was punishing you. But I knew God loved me. I knew I hadn't done anything to deserve punishment of this kind. But it didn't lessen the sting of Ninnah's words any.

Elkanah was aware of my situation and hurt feelings. And he tried to be understanding and supportive. He really did. When he handed out the portions for the sacrifice, he always gave me a double portion and always told me again how much he loved me. But he just didn't get it. Now, don't get me wrong. I loved Elkanah more than anything, and to hear him tell me again how beautiful I was and how much he loved me, well, that was wonderful. But he just didn't understand my agonizing need to have a child of my own. I know you know what I mean. There are just some things that only the LORD God or someone who's walked in your same shoes can understand. I often felt so useless, so lost. The more Ninnah irritated and taunted me, the more depressed I became. Some days all I wanted to do was cry. Other days, I couldn't eat or sleep or even think clearly.

That's what happened during one of my most memorable trips to Shiloh. I had spent my time during supper that evening just moving food around on my plate. I was feeling so heartbroken that I couldn't eat a bite. Finally, after supper, I headed to the temple to pray. I believe I was probably at the lowest point of my life. I thought that maybe if I prayed to the LORD once more, this time, things would get better. If I'm being honest, I don't think I really had any great expectations for a different outcome this time either. It's just that I was feeling so discouraged, so depressed, so desperate. I knew the LORD, and I knew that He was the only one I could turn to—the only one who could fully understand. Ninnah was the cause of a lot of the heartbreak, and Elkanah didn't fully comprehend the depth of my emotions and desires. Who else could I go to but God?

By the time I got to the temple that evening, I had been crying so hard and was so overcome with grief and anguish that the tears had stopped flowing. Words wouldn't come. I tried to speak, but all I could do was form the words with my lips and trust that God knew my heart and knew what I was saying. I was in so much distress as I prayed. I don't know if it was the grief or the anguish or what, but the words just silently spilled out of me. I was praying like I had never prayed before! Usually, when I prayed— although it was from my heart—it was filtered through my mind first before I spoke the words. This time, however, it seemed my prayers were taking a shortcut and going straight from my heart to God's heart. And then I heard myself praying something I'd never prayed before—and never dreamed I would pray. I vowed right then and there that if the LORD God would have favor on me and give me a son, I would give that son back to Him. In essence, he would be a Nazirite, living under the conditions of that vow, which included special dietary restrictions as well as never cutting his hair. After the words were out of my mouth, I had no choice but to carry through with my promise. Back in my day, if you vowed to do something, you did it. No questions asked. No backing out! As my husband, Elkanah could have nullified the vow, but he knew how important keeping it was to me. At the time, we had no clue if I would ever be in the situation where I would have to honor that vow. After all, I had prayed for children before and hadn't been blessed. I had even prayed for a child on previous trips to the temple. Why should this time be any different? But it was different—so very different!

I didn't know it at the time, but while I was praying, Eli, the priest, had been watching me. I think it's probably a good thing that I didn't know he was around, or I would have been too self-conscious. Anyway, because he didn't hear me praying out loud and only saw my lips move and my body shake from the anguish and sorrow, he thought I was drunk. So, he came over to me, told me to throw away my wine, and reprimanded me for coming into the temple while I was in such a state. I was shocked that he would think such a thing! Me, Hannah, a God-fearing woman who had never even come close to doing anything like what he was accusing me of! I assured him that I was not drunk—just overcome by sadness—and that I was pouring my heart out to God. He quickly apologized and was very understanding. Even today, I remember word for word what he said to me, "Cheer up! May the God of Israel grant the request you have asked of Him." I was so excited! My sadness disappeared in the blink of an eye, and I ran all the way back to the place where we were staying. I knew without a doubt the LORD had answered my prayer. I didn't know when I would see the answer. I only knew that someday I would have a child. That night I had never been happier—even happier than my wedding day!

Before you ask, yes, I was concerned about the vow. There was no way I could not be. Yet, I had a strange peace about it. It was almost as if I knew that when the time came, I would be strong enough to handle it. As it turned out, I didn't have to wait long to see how God was answering my prayer.

Early the next morning, the whole family got up and went to worship one last time before heading back home to Ramah. It wasn't until we got back home that Elkanah and I had some time alone. It was then that I told him about what had happened to me that last night at the temple. I told him everything—my anguish and desperation, my sorrow, my prayer, and my answer through Eli, the priest.

His reaction wasn't quite as over-the-top as I had expected, but he did seem mildly optimistic. He wanted it to be true—for me, more so than for himself. But I think he was afraid I was setting myself up for more disappointment. He loved me so much that it was the last thing he wanted me to experience again.

But Elkanah's reaction didn't discourage me at all—not after talking with Eli. After he said what he did, I just knew in my heart that my prayer was going to be answered. The only thing that surprised me, really, was how quickly it all came about. You know, we had not been back to Ramah very long before I began to suspect I might be pregnant. Then, as the months passed, it wasn't just my belly that grew but also my praise and adoration for such a loving and caring God. After all these years, He had seen it fit to shower me with the blessing of a child.

As you might guess, Ninnah's reaction wasn't nearly quite so joyous. She was not happy at all. She knew of Elkanah's love for me, and as long as she was the one bearing him children, she thought maybe she would eventually gain the upper hand and become his favorite.

But Elkanah—oh, you couldn't have asked for a better, more supportive husband. He was so attentive. As soon as he knew, he began treating me like royalty. He waited on me hand and foot and saw that others did the same. I'm sure he was afraid I might miscarry, but I had no fear of that. I knew in my heart this was the LORD's answer. I knew, at long last, I would have a child.

Yes, the vow was concerning, but it was never something I worried over. It's hard to explain, and I really don't expect you to understand, but I truly had peace. If I had a son, I knew the LORD would be with me and would help me be strong when the time came to give my baby back to Him. Then, when Samuel was born, I became convinced even more that God would help me because there was no way I would be able to do it on my own.

The name "Samuel" means "asked of the LORD." I wanted a name that clearly portrayed my feelings and yet also told his story. "Samuel" seemed to fit our circumstances perfectly—I had asked the LORD for him, and He had answered.

Samuel, of course, was incredibly special! Being my only child, I protected him with every ounce of strength I had. And Elkanah, well, he doted on him like you wouldn't believe. Samuel was a very special and delightful gift. He seemed to be so alert and advanced for his age, too. He understood things about God that were hard for me to comprehend. And smart, oh, he was smart! I spent those early years enjoying every minute with him.

From the first day, I had told Samuel how he came to be and how special he was. I made sure he understood the meaning behind his name and what the LORD God intended for his life. Then, when Samuel was about two, and it was time for the yearly sacrifice, I didn't go. Instead, I promised Elkanah that the next year, when Samuel was three, I would make the trip and would turn Samuel over to Eli for service to God. Just before he left that year, Elkanah said, "May the LORD help you keep your promise." That's when I knew how concerned he was. He never said so, but I suspect his prayer time at the temple that year was spent in large part praying not only for me but also for Samuel and our last year together as a family—that I would have the courage and strength to give back to the LORD this precious gift.

That last year went by so quickly. I prayed and cried myself to sleep more nights than I could count. When Elkanah told me it was time to prepare to go to Shiloh again, I couldn't believe our final year with Samuel was already over. It seemed like just yesterday they were all returning from last year's trip! But it was time. It was so hard to pack for that trip. I treasured everything of Samuel's as I put it in his bag. And I prayed almost constantly. I think his bag was as full of my tears as it was of anything else. I knew I would soon be facing, by far, the hardest thing in my life.

The days it took us to travel from Ramah to Shiloh were the longest of my life. All I could do was put one step in front of the other. With each step, I knew I was that much closer to the inevitable. I knew I had prepared both Samuel and myself as best I knew how. I just hoped it was enough. The evening we stepped through the city gate at

Shiloh, the sun was just setting. I remember thinking how appropriate that was. Our life with Samuel as we knew it was coming to an end as well. Tomorrow would be the day.

Needless to say, I didn't sleep at all that night. I was reminded of a previous trip to Shiloh—the one when I begged God for Samuel. Like that night, I could neither eat nor sleep. Tears of anguish just flowed down my cheeks. And just like before, by the time I got to the temple the next morning, my tears were all cried out. But unlike the last time, I was able to think and speak clearly.

After sacrificing a three-year-old bull, Elkanah and I each took one of Samuel's tiny little three-year-old hands and walked straight to Eli, the priest. Elkanah and Eli allowed me to speak and tell our story. I reminded Eli of the time we had met and told him what my prayer had been that day and how the LORD had answered through him. I told him of the vow and how I was ready to fulfill my part by turning Samuel over to the LORD God for service in the temple.

With deep understanding in his eyes, Eli bent down, took Samuel's hands, and the two of them began talking. As Elkanah and I were walking away, we turned and took one last look at our baby. What we saw—Eli and Samuel together praising God—both comforted and blessed us. Our hearts, although broken, were at peace. Before

Elkanah and I even got out the temple door, I couldn't help but praise God. He had given me the delight of my heart through Samuel, and now, even after all we had just been through, I again found myself rejoicing. I discovered a different kind of delight—one that comes from full obedience to God.

The trip home was long, but my heart was at peace. And every year from then on, when I went to the temple for our yearly sacrifices, I took along a new robe I had made for Samuel. And every year, Eli would say a special blessing over us and would pray that the LORD would bless us with more children. And, you know what? I ended up having three more boys and two girls—blessings each and every one. But, as you might guess, a big chunk of my heart always remained with Samuel.

In closing, my friend, I urge you to always trust God and be obedient to Him. Sometimes we may be asked to turn over our most precious treasure to Him. In my case, it was my child. For others, it might be something entirely different—a relationship or a dream you've had for a long, long time. I learned that if you let go of it with a heart that truly trusts God, He will fill the void with a joy you could not have thought or imagined.

And, honey, don't be afraid to tell God exactly how you feel. Even though He already knows, He wants to know that you love Him enough to be honest and open with Him about absolutely everything—the good, the bad, and the ugly. May God bless you, my precious friend.

Love always,
Hannah

Discussion/Reflection Questions

The following questions are designed to help you dig a bit more and think a little deeper. As the saying goes, "You will get out of this what you put into this." Don't short-change yourself. Take a few minutes to reflect on each of these questions and jot down your thoughts. If you are participating in a group study, consider sharing your discoveries with others in your small group.

You will notice reflection question #6 gives you the opportunity to write a return letter. This exercise is greatly encouraged because it will help you make a more personal connection.

1. Hannah was asked to turn over her precious three-year-old son to God. And, as unfathomable as it may seem, she did it with grace and dignity. Have you ever had to turn something precious over to God? If so, what was it, and how hard was that for you to do?

2. Just as in Bible times, we know that children are a gift from God. Our role as Christian parents is to nurture, train, and lead them to a point where we release them over to service for God, to do what He has planned for them. How is what we are asked to do with our children different

from or similar to what Hannah was asked to do?

3. Hannah found herself praying one of those "If you'll do this, God, then I'll do this" prayers. Have you ever prayed one of those "if-then" prayers? If so, what was that prayer? Has God taken you up on it? How?

4. Have you ever prayed for something for a long time, and God just didn't seem to be listening? If so, has God answered that prayer, or are you still waiting? If you're still in God's "waiting room," how can you be sure what you're praying is in accordance with God's will?

5. Hannah's inability to bear children caused a lot of heartache in her life. People in Bible times assumed her barrenness was punishment for some grievous sin she had committed. Others, like Peninnah, taunted her. How are childless women today treated differently from the way they were in Bible times? How are they treated similarly?

6. Now, it's your turn. Write a letter back to Hannah. Write whatever you want. This is your personal letter to her. Some suggestions: Thank her for sharing her story. Tell her what sharing her story meant to you. Ask her questions. Let her know in what ways you can identify

with her. Be imaginative!

NOTE: If you would like your letter to Hannah to be considered for publication in a future book, you may do so by emailing a copy directly to: cheryllelliott@gmail.com.

You will be contacted personally if your letter is chosen to be represented in the book.

Please note that the deadline for receiving these letters is June 1, 2024 for printing in a book to be tentatively released the fall of 2024.

Miriam

No Small Roles in God's Plan

Miriam's story is found in Exodus 1:6–2:10; 14:1–15:21;
Numbers 12:1–15; 20:1

My Dearest Friend,

It is so nice to be able to sit and "visit" with you a spell through this letter. I pray you and your family are doing well and that our God is blessing you beyond measure. When people ask me to tell them about my life, their favorite story is usually the one when I was a young girl hiding out near the Nile River, watching over Moses. So let me begin there. Although it happened many years ago, in some ways, it seems as if it was only yesterday.

I remember the morning I woke up to the sound of Mom sobbing. I couldn't imagine what had happened to get her so upset. Everything had seemed all right the night before. So, I got up and began to quietly tiptoe into her room. Dad met me just inside the door and told me that the baby had been born. A boy. That was all he needed to say for me to understand. You see, they really, really wanted a baby girl. If you know much about the culture I grew up in, then you know baby boys were what everyone wanted. So, it may seem strange to you when I tell you that Mom and Dad desperately wanted a baby girl. And so did I. I wanted a baby sister more than just about anything. After all, I already had a baby brother—what did I need another one of those for? What I *really* needed was a sister! But, sons were important because they grew up and became men with families of their own who carried on the family name. Daughters grew up to become wives and mothers to others. In a lot of cases, we girls were not considered much more than another piece of property.

Come to think about it, during that time in Israel's history, we were all pretty much considered pieces of property—all of us Israelites, that is. We had been in Egypt long enough that our ancestors, Joseph, and all his brothers, had died, and a new Pharaoh had come into power. This new king of Egypt didn't know (or didn't care—I'm not sure which) about Joseph and all he had done—especially his part in saving the whole nation of Egypt during a famine. Instead, all Pharaoh saw was a bunch of Israelites multiplying like crazy in *his* country.

I guess he saw us as a threat to taking over someday. Anyway, one of the first things he did was turn us into slaves, thinking that would keep us from having so many babies. I remember my dad coming home from work so tired and exhausted. Mom would rub his shoulders, trying to relax his tense, sore muscles. And many nights, he would fall asleep almost before supper was over. I felt so sorry for him. I would hear Mom and Dad talk about a better life. Oh, how they longed to have a life of freedom! They often told Aaron, my brother, and me stories they had grown up hearing about how life used to be before slavery. It sounded so wonderful. But instead of things getting better, they only got worse.

Then, shortly after Mom found out she was going to have another baby, Pharaoh declared, "Enough is enough!" He decided that if the Israelites could not or would not stop having children, he would do something about Israel's growth spurt once and for all. So, he commanded that the midwives kill all the Israelite boys the minute they were born. But the midwives were God-fearing women. They couldn't do that any more than you or I could kill an innocent baby. Well, when Pharaoh found out his latest plan wasn't working, he went even further and demanded that all the newborn Israelite boys be thrown into the Nile River and left to drown. So, you can understand now why Mom and Dad wanted a baby girl.

My parents agonized for days about what to do. They knew they had to do everything they could to keep him safe. I guess they were thinking—hoping—that the Israelites would somehow be set free before he was found out. Anyway, Mom and Dad knew their life had to remain as normal as possible so it wouldn't appear as if they were hiding something. So, that morning, Dad headed off to make bricks as usual, and Mom got up and did her normal activities. I cannot imagine how hard it must have been for her after just giving birth, but she did it. In so many ways, my mom taught me what strength was. You just do what you have to do when you have to do it. And if you rely on God, He will help you through it, no matter the situation.

When Mom went to the market, she would leave me in charge of my baby brother—Moses, as he came to be known later on. We kept him hidden in the house for weeks. The minute he even whimpered, we would do whatever we could to keep him quiet—give him something to eat, change him, hold him—anything and everything just so he'd stay quiet!

Then, when my brother was about three months old, Mom and Dad realized they could not hide him much longer. Each day he seemed to get louder and louder and more and more active. They knew it was just a matter of time before they were going to be found out, and he would be thrown into the river like the other baby boys. They were so desperate to do all they could to save their baby. Finally, one night, they devised a plan. The next morning, after Dad headed off to work, Mom wrapped baby Moses in a blanket and put him in a waterproof basket. Then, the two of us—Mom and I—casually walked to the river, where Mom carefully placed the basket among the reeds along the water's edge.

We purposely took Moses to an area of the river where we knew Pharaoh's daughter often bathed. Our prayer was that she would be the one to find him and that she would be kind and merciful toward him. I know it seems kind of counterintuitive to do this since it was her father who was having all the Israelite babies killed, but Mom and Dad were convinced this was the baby's best chance to survive. If another one of the Israelite women had found him, he would have been discovered and killed just as certainly as he would have been, had he remained with us. If one of the Egyptian women found him, what chance did she have of keeping an Israelite baby once Pharaoh found out? But the princess? Well, everyone knew Pharaoh doted on her. If anyone could sweet-talk him into not killing one of the Israelite baby boys, it was her. Mom saw the princess as the only chance she had of keeping her baby alive.

After placing Moses and the basket in the reeds, Mom couldn't risk staying there. If anyone saw her, they would have wondered why she was hanging around—that was something we kids did. So, Mom went back home while I was instructed to keep a close eye on the basket and let her know what happened. I was so nervous. And it seemed like I was there for such a long time, although I'm sure now it couldn't have been more than an hour or two. Then, finally, I saw the princess. I must admit I was excited at first. It was like I was playing a sort of spy game. But then, it began to embarrass me that I was watching her every move because she was, after all, there to bathe. Which, by the way, I always thought was odd. Why didn't she just take a bath back at the palace? Surely she had a place there where she could bathe with a lot more privacy. Anyway, I watched—and watched closely, mind you. After all, the princess was so close to the basket!

Then she saw it. That's when I began to hold my breath! What would she do? What would she think? A million thoughts ran through my mind. Then I began to think, *What if she saw me hiding and spying on her? Would she be mad? Would I get in trouble? How was I to get out of this predicament?* About that time, Pharaoh's daughter called for her servant girl to get the basket. That's when I knew I had the chance to make a move. So I came out from hiding and inched closer, making my presence known. I acted as if I was just a curious little Israelite girl out playing. The princess saw me but didn't say anything at first. I remember thinking I had gotten away with being a spy. But in hindsight, I wonder if, all along, the princess suspected who I was—the baby's sister.

Oops! I'm getting ahead of myself. Let me back up a bit in my story.

I knew the princess could hear my baby brother crying before she even looked inside the basket. After all, I could hear him from where I was! He did have a perfect set of lungs! But I still didn't know what kind of person the princess was. As it turned out, she fell in love with him the minute she saw him. And she suspected how he came to be in the river. She knew that there was some mother out there who saw this as her last hope to keep her son alive. And I think it melted her heart. Anyway, I heard her tell her servant girl that she was of half a mind to keep the baby herself but that she had a problem—he was too young and still needed to be nursed. When I heard that, I finally approached her and offered to get a Hebrew woman to nurse him for her. She thought that was the perfect solution and asked me to go get someone. And, of course, I headed straight home to get Mom! I ran as fast as my little legs would go.

As you can guess, I was so excited I literally burst through the door. I found Mom sitting in the corner next to the baby's things. But I didn't lose a beat. Even before my feet stopped, my mouth started talking. I was talking so fast that I'm surprised Mom could understand a word I said. Anyway, Mom was stunned at the turn of events. This was beyond her wildest dreams. So, she ran back with me to the princess, both of us hoping that she would still be there with our baby. And she was!

It was wonderful! The princess asked Mom if she would be willing to nurse Moses—for pay, of course—until he was weaned. *Moses*. That was the name she gave him. It means "to draw out." Appropriate, don't you think? Anyway, it was like a dream come true for us. Not only did we get Moses back, but Mom also got paid to care for him! Isn't it amazing how God can turn things around so completely? And to do it in the space of only a couple of hours! My mom went from devastating sorrow to overwhelming joy.

Dad had hurried home from work that day, expecting to find the worst. Instead, imagine his surprise to find the son he'd thought he'd lost! And, oh, the story Mom had to tell! Those few years with Moses went by much too quickly. We were so happy to be a complete family. I'm not sure Mom or Dad ever got to the point where they fully understood how compassionate God is. But then again, I'm not sure any of us do. We try, but there is no way our feeble minds can understand the depth of His love.

Anyway, it was such a relief not to have to hide Moses any longer! Now, Mom could take him with her everywhere she went. But that presented another set of problems. We learned to be careful around other women who had lost their sons at the hand of Pharaoh. We had to be understanding and sensitive to their feelings as well. It was quite a balancing act. But as time passed, things began to get easier.

Pharaoh's daughter kept in touch with us during those

early years. She always made sure Moses was cared for and had everything he needed. And Mom and Dad saw to it that he learned about his own family history as well. It seemed that every time we turned around, they were telling us stories about our ancestors—especially how we got to be in Egypt in the first place and how someday we would leave. Mom and Dad always knew that eventually, the Israelites would get back to their homeland. They just didn't know when—or how—it would happen. Mom would tell stories and sing favorite songs all the time— while she nursed Moses, while we played together, ate together, before going to bed. She and Dad took every opportunity to instill in us a love for God and the nation of Israel. They also let us know that there was nothing God couldn't handle or take care of. I could not have asked for better parents.

Almost before we knew it, the day we had been dreading came, and we had to give Moses up for good. It was so hard to do. We had become so attached to him. Later, I thought about how unfair it was that we had to give Moses up twice—once in the basket as an infant and again as a three-year-old to live in Pharaoh's palace with the princess.

After his move to the palace, we only saw Moses occasionally. Mom had prepared him for this time, so he knew that this was God's will for his life, even though none of us understood why at the time. It wasn't until many years later that we began to see how God's plan was unfolding. Meanwhile, Mom, Dad, Aaron, and I all watched from a distance. On the one hand, Mom and Dad were proud of him. On the other, they worried that he would forget his roots. On the one hand, Aaron and I adored him. On the other, we found ourselves becoming jealous of him.

Believe me when I tell you that I know jealously is not a good thing, but we couldn't seem to help ourselves. It just seemed as if Moses lived a life of privilege and stardom. He always seemed to be front and center, and that bothered us. He grew up in Pharaoh's palace; we grew up working our fingers to the bone as slaves. He grew up dressed in the finest clothes; we were lucky to get a new robe or sandals every couple of years. He ate the richest of foods; we ate the same old boring, tasteless food. And the biggie? Well, it's another long story. But let's just say that, even after Moses had killed a man, ran off to the land of Midian to escape punishment, and married a foreigner, God still chose him to lead us out of Egypt! We couldn't understand God's thinking. Besides that, as much as we loved Moses, he wasn't a leader by any stretch of the imagination! And you know what? Moses didn't see himself as a leader, either. When God told him what he was to do, the first thing Moses did was beg God to send someone else. But God had already planned for Moses to be the one to rescue the Israelites from the Egyptians. So, instead of sending someone else to do the job, God reluctantly agreed to allow Aaron to be by Moses' side and be his spokesman. The two of them began working together to bring about God's deliverance of the Hebrews. But it was Moses who got to meet and talk with God through the burning bush. He was the one who got to climb Mt. Sinai, again and again, to meet and talk directly with God. It was always Moses. He seemed to be in God's center of attention, and Aaron and I seemed to be on God's periphery.

Yes, I know I still sound jealous of Moses. And, at the time, I was. I'm not proud of it, but I'm just being honest and telling it the way it was. I did have an awful time adjusting to his authority. After all, he was my younger brother! It took me years, but I did finally get accustomed to taking orders from him. However, that didn't come without some moments of outright rebellion and resentment on my part. It's a wonder God put up with me! It was as much what I didn't do as it was what I did do. For instance, what I didn't do was realize—or rather, accept—the fact that Moses was God's choice in leading the people out of Egypt. I had known Moses from the day he was born and saw how human he was and the mistakes he had made.

I had trouble believing that God would choose someone like him to accomplish this humongous task. I guess it was all a little too hard for me to believe. I think it's hard for any brother or sister to accept the fact their sibling had celebrity status and they didn't. After all, you've grown up with them; you've seen their mistakes, their faults, their failures, their humanness.

The thing is, I focused more on the job God had called Moses to do and how God was working through him than I did on my own calling. I was a long time realizing that God had called me into another type of leadership position of my own. At the time, I was so blind and couldn't see what God might have in mind for me to do or how He was at work in my own life. It turns out all three of us—Moses, Aaron, and me—were being used by God.

I've often wished I had been a quick learner! But I wasn't. As soon as God set into motion His plan for our deliverance, one thing after another happened that always left me questioning God. For instance, one of the first things God expected Moses to do was get permission from Pharaoh for the Hebrews to leave the country. Moses knew that would not be easy. After all, we had been Pharaoh's slaves and major brick-builders for many, many years! He wasn't about to let the cheap labor go. But God—and Moses—were determined. I'll admit, I do have to give

Moses credit for that! He was persistent.

Time after time, Moses and Aaron approached Pharaoh, requesting permission to leave Egypt so we could worship as a nation. But, time after time, Pharaoh refused. And every time he refused, God sent a plague on the entire country—ten of them in all! It was downright awful. You name it; we had it—blood, frogs, gnats, flies, boils, hail, locusts—we had them all and more! Some of the plagues didn't affect the Israelites—only the Egyptians. But we could see and hear their agony. I always felt so sorry for the innocent Egyptians. A lot of them looked up to Moses and had great respect for him. They had to endure so much because of Pharaoh. He was so stubborn that, finally, what it took to get him to let us leave was a plague of death. We Israelites had been forewarned, so we knew to mark our doors. And about midnight one night, it happened. The firstborn males of all the Egyptians were instantly killed— from the Pharaoh's own palace to the Egyptian prisoners, even to the livestock. Well, that was the last straw. Pharaoh finally gave up. He immediately called for Moses and Aaron and demanded we leave!

Well, he didn't need to tell us twice! Moses had told us Israelites the day before to prepare to travel, so we were already pretty much packed up. And as we were leaving the country, we had been told to ask our Egyptian neighbors for silver, gold, and clothing. Which, by the way, they were more than willing to give! They were so eager to have us gone. They had realized, much sooner than Pharaoh, that all the plagues and problems they had been having were because of us. So, they wanted to be rid of us as soon as possible. We began marching out of Egypt even before daylight!

Oh, we celebrated big time! We were so excited to be leaving Egypt. But, as excited as we were, it wasn't long before we began to have serious doubts. More than once, people begged to turn back. Things got pretty bad at times. I can't begin to tell you everything we went through because there was a lot—good and bad—that happened over the span of forty years. So, I'll try to tell you a condensed version as best I can.

As you can imagine, it took several days for all of us to get out of Egypt. After all, there was a good bit of walking involved, and there were only a million or so of us! Once we were away from Egypt's borders, we expected God to take us on a direct route to our *promised land*. But He didn't! Instead, we headed through the wilderness toward the Red Sea. That's when the murmurings really began in earnest. We were all questioning Moses as to why we were taking the long way—especially given the number of women and children in the group. But Moses assured us that this was God's idea—not his—and that everything would be okay. During that time, we experienced a lot of tense situations. But God always seemed to come to our rescue at the last minute, with miracle after miracle, despite all of our whining. And, believe me, we did a lot of whining!

But God was faithful. He provided a cloud for us to follow each day and a pillar of fire at night. When we got to the Red Sea, we saw a huge obstacle. But God didn't. He parted the waters, and we walked across on dry ground—we didn't even have mud or puddles to worry about. Later, when we complained about food, we received bread straight from heaven's oven. And, would you believe, once when we were thirsty, God provided water from a rock? Then there was the time we won a battle just because Moses kept his arms raised. That was a biggie! After our victory, Moses led the people in a song of praise, and then I grabbed my tambourine and led all the women in rhythm and dance. It was really quite a celebration! But it didn't last. Even with all the miracles, we Israelites kept complaining. We were tired of camping out, and many times we begged to go back to Egypt. And, I'll be completely honest, I think I may have been the worst complainer of all.

I say that because of one particularly embarrassing incident that stands out in my mind. Remember, we had been on the road for quite some time. We were tired—all of us! One day Aaron and I were especially out of sorts, and the two of us began criticizing Moses about his choice of wives. As I reflect on that, it was really such a petty thing to complain about. In our defense, at the time, we were all so tired from traveling around, and we were so frustrated because there seemed to be no end in sight. Anyway, Aaron and I began to feed on each other's egos with reminders of how God had used *us* during these wanderings—acting as if we were just as important as Moses.

Aaron and I hadn't stopped to think that God could hear every word coming out of our mouths. But He did. And, boy, was He mad! God immediately called us on the carpet. He told all three of us to go into the portable tabernacle. Then He came down in the form of a cloud and blocked the entrance so we couldn't get out. He called Aaron and me forward and straightened us out about who was who, once and for all. God left no doubt as to who He wanted in charge, and it wasn't either one of us! And then, as if to emphasize what He said, He caused me to get leprosy. I turned white as a sheet and began to develop sores all over my body. Aaron began begging for forgiveness from Moses; Moses began begging God for mercy for me and my healing. God then told Moses to banish me from the camp for seven days. Only after that could I return to camp.

During those seven days, I did a lot of thinking and praying, believe me! Even though it was hard and I hated it, it was probably the best thing for me. It was during this time that I settled in my mind who was in charge and what my role had been all along. To my surprise, I discovered that my role had been the same one that I'd had back when Moses was a baby being placed in the basket in the Nile River. I was to support Moses by standing along the sidelines at a distance and seeing what would happen. My job was to encourage him and stand by his decisions, trusting that God was at work through him. During those seven days of banishment (which I prefer to call a retreat because it sounds better), so many lessons came to mind. I think God knew I needed that time alone, just Him and me, so I could hear Him clearly and reflect on what I was learning (or should have already learned). My dear friend, one of the most important lessons I learned during my lifetime was that there are no small roles in God's plan. I would encourage you to learn what it is God expects you to do and strive to do it to the best of your ability.

Along the same line, I encourage you to accept and support those whom God places in authority over you. Believe me, I wasted a lot of years before wholeheartedly accepting Moses' authority. But in the end, I became one of his biggest fans! Also, I learned to back off and allow

God the freedom to work in His own way, in His own time. For seven days, the Israelites—and Moses—managed without me and my input. It was hard for me to accept, but I learned that things turned out a whole lot better when I stepped back and let God take over.

My friend, no matter what is going on in your life, please remember that God is good. It is so hard for us to understand why we must go through trying times or circumstances, but it's important that we trust God. Although painful, these things must happen to strengthen and refine us. God's purpose is to bring about what is best for us, our family members and friends, and ultimately His glory. I close this letter with a humble heart and a prayer that God would richly bless and comfort you on your own life's journey.

Love to you always,
Miriam

Discussion/Reflection Questions

The following questions are designed to help you dig a bit more and think a little deeper. As the saying goes, "You will get out of this what you put into this." Don't short-change yourself. Take a few minutes to reflect on each of these questions and jot down your thoughts. If you are participating in a group study, consider sharing your discoveries with others in your small group.

You will notice reflection question #6 gives you the opportunity to write a return letter. This exercise is greatly encouraged because it will help you make a more personal connection.

1. Miriam speaks so lovingly of her mother's strength and belief in God. One of the lessons her mother taught her was that if she relied on God, He would help her through any situation or problem that came up. If you grew up in a Christian home, what lessons about God did your mother pass on to you?

2. One thing Miriam noticed as a young girl was how quickly God could turn a situation around. In just a short time, she saw her mother go from extreme sorrow to extreme joy. Have you ever had a situation in which

your emotions plummeted and then skyrocketed at such amazing speeds that it left you in awe of God?

3. Early on, Miriam gave Moses credit for his persistence in approaching Pharaoh. Have you ever been persistent in a situation? How long did that season last? In looking back, are you 100 percent sure it was God's will that you persisted?

4. Miriam noted through the wilderness wanderings that God doesn't always work in the way that seems best to us. Have you ever been in a situation when you wondered just why God was leading you in the direction He was? Why do you think God will often take people on the "scenic route" instead of the shortcut?

5. As Christians, we are all God's representatives. Miriam learned the hard way that there are no small roles in God's plan. We each have a unique part we are expected to fulfill. What role—or roles—do you feel God has assigned you in order to further His plans?

6. Now, it's your turn. Write a letter back to Miriam. Write whatever you want. This is your personal letter to her. Some suggestions: Thank her for sharing her story.

Tell her what sharing her story meant to you. Ask her questions. Let her know in what ways you can identify with her. Be imaginative!

NOTE: If you would like your letter to Miriam to be considered for publication in a future book, you may do so by emailing a copy directly to: cheryllelliott@gmail.com.

You will be contacted personally if your letter is chosen to be represented in the book.

Please note that the deadline for receiving these letters is June 1, 2024 for printing in a book to be tentatively released the fall of 2024.

Esther

For Such a Time as This

Esther's story is found in Esther 1–10

My Dearest Friend,

Thank you for your previous letter asking me to share my story. I am very honored and humbled to do so. You addressed me as "Queen Esther," and while that was officially my title, I much prefer to be known simply as Esther. The royal title given me only reflected my position in life—a position I seemed destined to have in order to fulfill what God intended me to do. In reality, I'm just like any other woman, with the same feelings and emotions you have. While our appearances and experiences in life may have varied, deep down, we all have similar hopes and dreams for our lives and our families. We all experience seasons of sorrow as well as joy.

My early years were rough. Tragically, I lost both of my parents when I was very young. I only vaguely remember them. But I had a wonderful older cousin, Mordecai, who kindly took me in and cared for me as if I was his own daughter.

Years earlier, my people—the Jews—had been taken into captivity and were exiled to Persia. Even though we later gained our freedom and could have gone back to Jerusalem, Mordecai chose to stay. And since he was now my guardian, I stayed as well. That explains how I, a Jew, ended up being in Persia during the time King Xerxes (also known as King Ahasuerus) was searching for a new queen. The former queen, Vashti, was relieved of her royal position because she refused to obey the command of the king. The story goes that King Xerxes had just spent six months showing off his vast wealth, followed by seven days of partying and drinking with all the nobles and officials. On the last day, when the king was quite drunk, he asked Queen Vashti to make an appearance and join him and his partying friends so he could show her off because she was so beautiful. She refused. She may have refused in part because she was throwing a banquet for the women and didn't want to leave her own guests. But I think the main reason she didn't go was because she knew King Xerxes and his friends had been partying and drinking heavily and would be extremely drunk. And that was the last situation any woman wanted to place herself in. So, she refused, and I don't blame her.

Her refusal to come when summoned created quite a commotion throughout the palace. King Xerxes was furious! In my day, submission on the wife's part was not only expected—it was demanded. King Xerxes consulted with all his advisors, and, to make a long story short, Queen Vashti was thrown out of the palace quicker than anything. It seems all the bigwigs thought that what Queen Vashti had done would trickle down, and, before you knew it, women everywhere would start being disrespectful to their husbands. Queen Vashti's actions shocked the entire Persian Empire.

Well, after King Xerxes sobered up and cooled down a bit, he realized what a rash—and poor—decision he had made. After all, what kind of a king didn't have a queen in the palace, ready to stand by his side and do his bidding? He had to keep up appearances, you know. But he couldn't take Queen Vashti back. After all, how would that look? Any decree he made from that point on would have been looked upon as negotiable. People would always wonder if he really meant what he said or if he would later change his mind. So, he felt as if he had to stick to his own orders— even if they were made in the heat of the moment. King Xerxes found himself caught between a rock and a hard place. He didn't have a queen, and he couldn't reinstate Queen Vashti. What was he to do? Well, he decided to have the most beautiful women in Persia brought into his harem with the intention of finding a replacement queen from among them.

As you probably already know, I was chosen as one of those women. Even though I wasn't Persian, I had lived in Persia my entire life, so many people thought I was. And when I was selected, I didn't tell them any differently because Cousin Mordecai had advised me not to. Even though I wasn't sure what his reasoning was, I trusted him completely. In retrospect, I'm sure it was God who had laid it on Mordecai's heart that this bit of news needed to remain a secret from the palace officials.

It was so hard to leave my family and friends. And one of the worst things was that everything happened so suddenly that I didn't get a chance to say goodbye. I was so unhappy and felt so alone. Before I knew it, I was put in a harem with a lot of other young women and was placed under the care of a man named Hegai. He was the eunuch in charge of my beauty treatments. I was never one to focus a great deal on my looks, so this was all new territory for me. I soon learned that it was customary for any woman who was to be presented to the king to go through a whole year's worth of beauty treatments first. I personally thought that was a bit extravagant. Anyway, it was assumed that you were in the harem of the king because you were vying to become the next queen—which I was not! When it came down to it, I wasn't sure why I was there. I really had no thought or desire to be queen.

Everything seemed to happen so suddenly, and I was just going with the flow. At first, I felt as if I was caught up in a whirlwind. Then, when the beauty treatments began, my life seemed to come to a screeching halt. Suddenly, now I was spending long, boring days being rubbed down with oils. There wasn't much for us girls to talk about.

After all, we were secluded and protected from the outside world. So, day in, day out, I sat there listening to the other girls gush and swoon over the king and talk about how they hoped they would be the chosen one. That went on for six long months! Then after that, I spent another six months undergoing special treatments with perfumes and ointments, listening to more of the same jibber-jabber. I was nearly bored out of my mind! Maybe things would have been different if I'd shared the lofty goal they had. The other girls didn't seem to mind the excessive pampering at all—probably because they were so hopeful to be the next "Mrs. Xerxes." But that was the farthest thing from my mind. All I could think was, *What in the world am I doing here?* I was so homesick. So lonely. So bored.

The day I was crowned queen was another one of those whirlwind experiences I always seemed to find myself getting caught up in. After the year of pampering was over, I was presented to the king. The next thing I knew, the crown was placed on my head, and a big banquet was thrown in my honor. I could not believe the king had chosen me over all the other girls. I didn't know what to do. I'd obviously never been a queen before. How was I supposed to act? What was required of me? So many questions kept dashing through my brain. But, as it turned out, I didn't need to worry about any of them because just as suddenly as it all happened, it all stopped. I was dismissed until the king called for me again. Just like that! One minute I was the center of attention, and the next minute, it seemed, I'd been put in storage—only to be taken out again if the king called for me.

During that first year, Mordecai became a palace official. I was so thankful that I got to hear from him occasionally. Other than that, my life was rather isolating. So, my life went back to being boring. But you know, I came to appreciate boring days—especially after my next whirlwind experience!

It all began when King Xerxes promoted a man named Haman to be prime minister. That, in essence, made him the second most powerful official in the Persian Empire. Haman was a man with a big head. It wasn't too long until he had manipulated King Xerxes to declare that all the other officials in the palace were to bow down to him just as they did in the presence of the king. And they did— except for my cousin Mordecai, that is. When Mordecai was questioned about his refusal to bow before Haman, he said it was because he was a Jew. This made Haman furious. In fact, he was so mad that he plotted to have all the Jews in the empire killed. Of course, key to the success of this mission was the king himself. Haman went to King Xerxes and told him that there was a race of people living in

Persia who refused to obey the king's laws. Then he urged King Xerxes to see to it that these people were destroyed. Haman even bribed him, saying that if the king did him this one favor, he would give a good bit of money to the treasury. So, King Xerxes, without bothering to investigate the matter, handed over his royal seal to Haman, giving him authority to make decrees on behalf of the king. Of course, the first thing Haman did was turn around and dictate letters stating that by the time one year had passed, every Jew in Persia was to be killed.

When Mordecai got wind of this, he went into a state of deep mourning for all the Jews in Persia. He tore his clothes, put on sackcloth and ashes, and began crying and wailing. I had no clue what was going on until one of my maids came and told me about Mordecai's actions. Without knowing why he was in mourning, I sent him a fresh set of clothes. When Mordecai refused them, I sent one of the king's eunuchs to find out what was going on. Mordecai showed him a copy of the decree and asked the eunuch to take it and explain to me what it meant. He also told the eunuch to urge me to go to the king and beg for mercy for the Jews. Believe me, that was the last thing I wanted to do.

I was terrified when I learned what Mordecai expected of me. He and I both knew that absolutely no one in their right mind ever appeared before the king without first being summoned. If they did, and the king did not hold out his gold scepter as a sign of approval, that person would die. It had been over a month since the king had last called for me, so I wasn't at all sure I would be welcomed. Instead, I sent the eunuch back to Mordecai to explain my situation. I thought if Mordecai knew that the king hadn't called for me lately, he would understand and would find another solution. I honestly thought Mordecai would think of another way to get around the edict.

But Mordecai countered with what was actually a rather good argument. He reminded me that I, myself, was a Jew—and being the queen wasn't going to be enough to save even me. After all, the order had been for the annihilation of *all* the Jews. Mordecai was convinced God would rescue them somehow—if not through me, then through someone else. Then he suggested that maybe this was the reason I—a Jew—was in the palace in the first place. He said that, perhaps, this was God's way of preparing our nation for this day.

Although it seemed Mordecai was laying a heavy guilt trip on me, deep down, I always knew I was in the palace for some greater purpose. I just didn't know what— or when—I would find out. And I certainly didn't expect something that could cost me my life!

I spent a lot of time pacing the floor and thinking on what Mordecai suggested and how best for me to approach the king. Finally, I sent word back to Mordecai that I would go see King Xerxes, and if I died because of it, then so be it. However, before I went, I passed along to Mordecai a message letting him know that my servant girls and I would fast and pray. And I asked Mordecai to see to it that he and the other Jews did the same.

I was sick with fear. I fasted. I prayed. And I wracked my brain trying to figure out the best strategy so I would be sure of a favorable response from King Xerxes. It was, by far, the hardest thing I'd ever been asked to do. Honestly, I wasn't at all sure I was up to the task.

Three days later, after first getting my backup plan in motion just in case I chickened out, I slowly walked through the inner court of the palace and up to the king's hall. There I stood, shaking like a leaf and praying like you wouldn't believe that the king would accept me and hold out his gold scepter.

I stood there for what seemed like an eternity, although I'm sure it was only a few seconds—a minute at the most. My hands were sweaty, my knees felt like they would buckle under me any minute, and my heart was beating so loudly my head and ears were pounding. I honestly thought I was going to pass out. But just at that moment, I saw the gold scepter lift. I could hardly believe my eyes! He was holding out the scepter for me! I took a deep breath, got my bearings, mustered my courage, and walked toward the king until I was able to touch the tip of the scepter and bow before him. The king then asked me what I wanted and told me he would give me whatever it was—up to half the kingdom! How I wished that was what I was about to ask. That would have been so much easier. Anything would have been easier than what I needed to ask. Instead, I had come with a much greater, more life-threatening need. But, as I feared, I chickened out, and instead of asking him to rescind his degree to have the Jews killed, I invited the king to a banquet I would prepare the next day. I also asked him to bring along Haman, his right-hand man. And he agreed. Thank goodness for backup plans!

At the banquet the next day, while King Xerxes and Haman were eating, drinking, and thoroughly enjoying themselves, King Xerxes asked me what I wanted. It threw me for a loop when the king himself brought up the subject. You see, according to tradition, it was *my* responsibility to approach King Xerxes with any request, not vice-versa. I was tongue-tied for a few seconds. All the while, I had two sets of eyes just staring at me, wondering, waiting in anticipation to hear what I was going to ask. Well, again, I backed out and instead asked if he and Haman would come to yet another banquet I would prepare for them the next day. I could tell King Xerxes was getting very curious. So I promised him that the next day I would let him know what it was I wanted. That seemed to satisfy him, and it also gave me a bit more time. Believe me, that night I did some major praying—again!

Meanwhile, God was at work on two other fronts! Now comes the part where I think my backup plan was God's first plan all along. To begin with, after leaving that first banquet, Haman was on cloud nine. He was feeling especially important and began bragging about how I had invited only him and the king to a special banquet and how he had another invitation for the very next day. Haman reminded everyone he ran into about how he had been promoted above all the others in the palace. There seemed to be no end to his gloating. Then, in his typical self-absorbed fashion, in the next breath, he whined to all his family and friends that all the glory and prestige were meaningless as long as Mordecai was at the palace gate, refusing to bow to him. So, Haman's wife and friends suggested that he have gallows built and ask the king for permission to have Mordecai hanged. Well, as you can imagine, Haman thought that was a grand idea and instructed his men to get right on it.

Then, the second way God was at work happened

later that night. The king was having trouble sleeping, so he had an attendant read to him from some historical records. Personally, that would have done the trick for me right then and there! I would have fallen asleep in no time. But the king was still wide awake. So, the attendant continued reading and just "happened" to read the part about Mordecai and how he had earlier exposed an assassination plot against the king. King Xerxes asked how Mordecai had been rewarded and learned that nothing had ever been done to repay or honor him for his diligence. This oversight continued to weigh heavily on the king's mind. When Haman came strutting through the palace doors the next morning, King Xerxes asked him what should be done to show honor to a man the king is pleased with. Well, Haman thought for sure he was the man King Xerxes was referring to, so he presented some grandiose ideas—royal robe, royal horse with royal emblem on its head, royal parade through town. You get the idea. Imagine Haman's surprise when he found out it wasn't him at all but Mordecai the king wanted to honor. And not only that, but the king expected Haman himself to carry out the royal treatment of Mordecai!

Well, Haman did his duty. But, as soon as the grand procession was over, Haman made a beeline for the comforts of home with his tail between his legs and whined to his wife and friends about all that had happened. Everyone now saw the writing on the wall—it was no use for Haman to have ill thoughts about Mordecai now that the king had bestowed such honor on him. So Haman's wife and friends urged him to get over it and move on.

Haman was still bemoaning everything that was going on and feeling sorry for himself when his ride came to pick him up and bring him to my second banquet. I'm sure partying with the king was the last thing he felt like doing right then. Keep in mind that I didn't know any of these things had happened. I had spent the last few hours preparing for the next banquet and readying myself to tell the king what I wanted. Imagine my surprise to see the change in Haman. The day before, he had acted as if he was the life of the party. This time he seemed very subdued and downtrodden. The change in him really puzzled me.

Shortly into the meal, the king asked what I wanted. I think his curiosity was about to get the best of him. He even reminded me again that whatever it was, he would give it to me—up to half the kingdom! I'm sure he thought that would ease my mind and make it easier for me.

But it didn't. Oh, I was flattered that he was making such an effort to reassure me. But he had no clue of the seriousness of what I was about to ask. However, I knew that this time, it was now or never. I'm not sure King

My Dearest Friend

Xerxes would have accommodated me a third time. I told him about the situation the Jews were in and begged him to spare our lives. He asked whose idea it was to destroy them in the first place. When I told him it had been Haman who manipulated the decree, you should have seen the looks on both their faces. Haman turned white as a sheet, whereas King Xerxes turned fiery red. King Xerxes immediately jumped up to walk off his rage in the palace garden before he said or did anything rash. I think he remembered the last time he did something rash he lost his queen. Meanwhile, Haman began begging me for his life and pleading for mercy. In despair, he fell onto the couch where I was sitting. This happened the exact moment King Xerxes walked back in. Seeing Haman on the couch with me, and thinking he was assaulting me, made King Xerxes even more furious. So, he signaled that Haman was to be killed. That's the moment when both King Xerxes and I first learned from one of the eunuchs about the gallows Haman had his friends build. So King Xerxes ordered that Haman be hanged on them just as Haman had intended for Mordecai.

Thankfully, things did finally calm down—at least a little bit. Mordecai was given the king's signet ring, which King Xerxes had taken away from Haman, and I was given all of Haman's property. I immediately put Mordecai in charge of my new estate since I knew absolutely nothing about property management.

The thing of it is, in all the excitement, I never did get an answer from King Xerxes about rescinding the order regarding the Jews being killed! Would you believe I had no choice but to approach the king again? And, again, he received me. And, yet again, I asked favor for the Jews. This time King Xerxes had Mordecai write up an order to cancel out Haman's and had Mordecai seal it with the same signet ring that had once been given to Haman. He also made sure that Mordecai understood that this time, whatever was written could not be revoked—ever. I wish you could have seen and heard the celebration as news of the release of their death sentence spread to the Jews throughout Persia.

Whew! Reliving that story was exhausting. But I share it with you because I feel certain God wants me to encourage you. Most of the time, we are not privileged to see how God is working behind the scenes in our lives until the final act is played. Trust God completely. I see now that it was God who was causing me to keep putting off asking King Xerxes to spare the lives of the Jews. God needed to lay a little more groundwork to ensure that I would receive a favorable response. Don't rush God. And don't try to do everything yourself. Rely on Him. Learn to hear His voice.

Allow Him to take the lead. Your job is to follow.

My friend, although I don't believe you would ever have a problem with this, I would say to beware of getting a big head. Haman had finagled his way up to the position as King Xerxes' right-hand man. In so doing, he began to think himself invincible and better than anyone else—especially the Jews. When God looks at us, He doesn't see race or positions or knowledge or beauty or bank accounts. He sees hearts. Instead of having a big head, strive to have a big heart.

Write back when you get a chance! You are one special friend.

All my love,
Esther

Discussion/Reflection Questions

The following questions are designed to help you dig a bit more and think a little deeper. As the saying goes, "You will get out of this what you put into this." Don't short-change yourself. Take a few minutes to reflect on each of these questions and jot down your thoughts. If you are participating in a group study, consider sharing your discoveries with others in your small group.

You will notice reflection question #6 gives you the opportunity to write a return letter. This exercise is greatly encouraged because it will help you make a more personal connection.

1. Early on, Esther requested that her title as "Queen" be dropped. She pointed out that she was just Esther, a woman much like us. What kind of feelings and emotions did you notice as she told her story? Was she right? Do we average, modern women run the same gamut of emotions as she did even though she was a queen?

2. Congratulations! You've just won a year's worth of pampering at Healthy Spa Beauty Ranch. Visitors, phone calls, and mail are not allowed, so you can spend the whole time totally relaxed, mentally as well as physically. Do you

accept the prize? Why or why not?

3. In the space of what appears to be only a few short years, Esther recounts at least three whirlwind experiences she went through—being taken to the palace and placed in a harem, being chosen as the next queen a year later, and all the celebration that ensued, and witnessing firsthand the uproar at her second banquet when Haman's plans—past, present, and future—came to light. What whirlwinds have you experienced in your life?

4. When King Xerxes learned about Haman's actions, he became so infuriated that he had to walk away from the situation for a while. Have you ever had to walk away from a situation before you dared open your mouth? Or have you ever *not* walked away when you should have? Summarize the situation.

5. As Christians, we know that God can work all things out for good. What has happened in your life that you can look back on now and see how God was orchestrating the whole thing all along—people, timing, results, and so forth?

6. Now, it's your turn. Write a letter back to Esther.

Write whatever you want. This is your personal letter to her. Some suggestions: Thank her for sharing her story. Tell her what sharing her story meant to you. Ask her questions. Let her know in what ways you can identify with her. Be imaginative!

NOTE: If you would like your letter to Esther to be considered for publication in a future book, you may do so by emailing a copy directly to: cheryllelliott@gmail.com.

You will be contacted personally if your letter is chosen to be represented in the book.

Please note that the deadline for receiving these letters is June 1, 2024 for printing in a book to be tentatively released the fall of 2024.

Ruth

Blessing Following Heartache

Ruth's story is found in Ruth 1–4

My Dearest Friend,

How good to hear from you! I had to chuckle when you wrote that one of the reasons you admired me was because of my loving relationship with my mother-in-law. You might be surprised to learn that things weren't always rosy-rosy between Naomi and me. It's kind of a long story, but initially, there was a lot of friction between the two of us. We were very different people. She, of course, was older and from Israel; I was younger and from Moab. I'll spare you the long history lesson, but, in a nutshell, I'll just say that during my lifetime, the Moabites and Israelites basically despised each other. So much so, in fact, that it was against their law to have any association with us "idolatrous Moabites."

Elimelech, Naomi, and their two sons, Mahlon and Kilion, had traveled to Moab due to a severe famine that was going on in Israel at the time. Under the circumstances, you can imagine how bad the famine must have been for them, as well as several other families, to even consider moving to Moab. Their original plan had been to live in Moab—just a short time—only until the famine was over. Then they had planned to head back home. But as the years went by and as their sons grew to become young men, not only did they remain in Moab, but they also sought wives for their sons in the hopes of becoming grandparents to grandsons to carry on the family name. I think their plan had been to find women from among the other Israelite families who had resettled in Moab. But Mahlon and I had an immediate attraction to one another. I knew there would be struggles along the way because of our very different backgrounds, but I also knew we could work through them together.

Naomi didn't like it at all when Mahlon and I became good friends. It wasn't until after her son and I were married that Naomi and I began to slowly develop a kinda-sorta friendly relationship. Just when it seemed as if we were beginning to adjust to one another, Elimelech, Naomi's husband and Mahlon's dad, died rather suddenly. That shocked all of us. My first instinct was to run to the gods I had grown up with and try to appease them with sacrifices so the curse would be lifted from the family. But Naomi would have none of that. She let me know in no uncertain terms that if I was going to be a part of their family, then I was going to be expected to worship as they did. At first, I didn't like being told what I could or couldn't do. And I especially had trouble understanding how Naomi, Mahlon, and Kilion (Mahlon's brother) could still praise and worship God after such a tragedy. Oh, my friend, they were so patient with me. I shudder to think how different my life would have been had it not been for them.

At the time, I couldn't see how anything good could ever happen without first offering sacrifices to the gods. Naomi called it idolatry and said it was wrong—really wrong. Instead, she insisted I worship the "one true God," as she called Him. It was all so confusing. But even so, during this time, I noticed a big difference in how we mourned. While Naomi was certainly devastated and heartbroken, Elimelech's death did not destroy her. She kept her head up, squared her shoulders, and moved on, doing what needed to be done. She knew and believed that everything was in God's hands and that He would continue to provide for her just as He would continue to love and care for her. I was not so optimistic at first. I had trouble understanding how you worshipped a god you couldn't see or touch. But because I loved Mahlon so much, I was willing to give up my idols in search of Naomi's one true God.

Gradually I came to love the same God Naomi and her sons did. As time passed, we began to settle into a routine and started living as one big, happy family. It wasn't too long after we were married that Kilion also married. His wife's name was Orpah, and she was also a Moabite. The next few years were wonderful. However, neither Orpah nor I gave birth to children. But I did feel as if I had been given a new birth. And I guess in a way I had because I came to personally know Naomi's God. I made a mental decision that I would never go back to idol worship. Oh, how I was tested in the days and years to come.

Tragedy struck our family again. And again. Two punches—back-to-back. That's when both Mahlon and Kilion died. Their deaths left us spinning. In such a short time, we went from being a happy family of five down to three—all women. We weren't sure what we were going to do. We had so many questions. Why would God allow this to happen to us? And without a man around, how would we ever be able to provide for ourselves? Back in our day, widowed women were destined to live a life of poverty. And to top it off, Orpah and I had no sons who could grow up to care for us. It was after I became widowed that I came to truly rely on Naomi and the God she talked about to get me through the heartache.

Meanwhile, Naomi was in such anguish that she could hardly think straight! After all, she had lost not only her husband but two sons as well. And, to top it off, she was still living in a foreign land. She asked a lot of questions of God those first few days and weeks. Things like, "Why did this happen?" "Couldn't one of them have been spared?" "Why them? Why not me?" "Am I being punished for coming to Moab in the first place?" "How am I to survive?" But through all her grief, Naomi stuck by God, believing that, in the end, everything would be okay.

During this time, Orpah and I were very tempted to run back home to our families and idol worship. But we didn't! That was such a milestone. Even though we were so new in our faith and had to rely on Naomi to get us through, we—and she—did. We all got through it! It wasn't easy by any means, and we spent some long hours talking, crying, and praying. But God was faithful. It wasn't too long afterward when Naomi learned that the famine in Israel was over. Not surprisingly, she decided to head back home. That's when things really began to get interesting!

Early on, Naomi had decided that the three of us would pack up and head to Bethlehem, the town in Israel where she had come from. But as soon as we got on the road and started on the long journey, Naomi seemed to change her mind. She told Orpah and me to turn around and go back home to our families. We told her that we wouldn't—couldn't—that we were now her family and she was ours and that we wanted to go with her to her homeland. But she insisted. Finally, Orpah was persuaded to return, but I just couldn't. Naomi kept reminding me that she had no more sons for me to marry. And she wasn't sure what, if any, family members remained in Israel who could redeem the family of Elimelech. She wanted to release me so I would be able to marry again within my own nationality. Her thoughtfulness and kindness left me almost overwhelmed. At a time when her life was in such turmoil and uncertainty, her first thoughts were for Orpah and me—that we be free to remarry and go on with our lives and hopefully have children someday. But I had come to love Naomi so much that I couldn't imagine my life without her. Through my tears I mumbled something about going where she would go and dying where she would die and being buried where she would be buried and serving the same God she served. At the time, the possibility of remaining single for the rest of my life or never having children didn't seem important. And I was okay with the thought of possibly never seeing my biological family or friends or homeland again. I realized later that, while all those things were important, what I wanted more than anything was to not be separated from Naomi—or God. I knew that if I went back home, I would lose both. In the few years I had known and been a part of Naomi's family and had come to know God, I was convinced that He was, indeed, the one true God, just as Naomi had claimed. How thankful I am that Naomi and Mahlon introduced me to Him.

Even after all this, Naomi still wasn't too thrilled to have me tagging along with her back to Bethlehem. I think she feared the uncertainty and potential life that was ahead for us. But I really didn't give her much of a choice! It was almost as if I was a little girl hanging onto her mother's apron strings. I wasn't about to let her go! In retrospect, I wonder if maybe this was some sort of test—to see if I loved God only with my mind or if I truly loved Him with my whole being—heart, soul, and mind.

The trip to Bethlehem was long and hard. And when we arrived, Naomi was immediately the center of attention. It seemed everyone had heard about her misfortune in losing not only her husband but also her sons. When she had left Israel years before, she was married and secure. Now she was widowed and poor. Life was not turning out at all the way she had expected. However, Naomi had many old friends who came by and mourned with her. They all felt so sorry for her. I could tell Naomi was loved and well thought of. But early on, it seemed to me as if these friends of hers made an already bad situation worse.

You see, her friends showed her such pity that she asked to be called "Mara," which meant "bitter," instead of being referred to by her given name of Naomi, which meant "pleasant." It was as if her friends fed her self-pity. And I must say, for a time, "Mara" did seem to fit her better. But I learned that this was a part of the grieving process Naomi had to go through. Bottom line: even at her lowest, Naomi still trusted God. Before too long, our situation improved, and we began to settle into our new life. Then, almost before we knew it, our lives took a drastic and sudden change for the better. God certainly does take care of those He loves.

It all started not too long after we had settled in Bethlehem. The visitors had dwindled down, and Naomi and I realized that we were going to have to do something or find some way to start providing for ourselves—especially to get some food for the table. That's when I came up with the idea to go to the fields and pick up the leftover grain that had fallen to the ground. I knew it would be hot, dirty, hard work. And I knew that my efforts may or may not give us much food to eat. But it was all I could think to do at the time. And besides, Naomi was too old and too frail to be expected to go out and do such work. Our long trip had taken a toll on her physically. I really worried about her. Anyway, Naomi reluctantly agreed, so off I went.

Would you believe I just "happened" to end up at the field of a man named Boaz, who just "happened" to be from the clan of Elimelech—Naomi's husband? I had no idea who he was, and at first, he wasn't sure who I was either! After asking the overseer of his harvesters about me, Boaz told me to glean only from his field, to follow along behind his harvesters, and to only glean alongside his servant girls. At the time, I still didn't know that he was a relative of Naomi's, so it really puzzled me as to why he would be so kind to me, a foreigner. He told me that, whenever I was thirsty, to drink from the water jars his men had already filled. He even offered me some food, and after I ate, I went back to gleaning the field, doing as Boaz had said.

It wasn't until later that night, after I had gone back home to Naomi, that I learned who Boaz was. Earlier, when I asked Boaz why he was being so kind to me, he only said that it was because he had heard about me and how I had left my homeland to follow Naomi and live with and take care of her. I learned later that he had told his workers to "accidentally" drop extra grain for me to gather. After I was done gleaning that first day, I ran home to Naomi to show her how much I had gathered in just one day's work.

I wish you could have seen her face! Naomi took one look at the huge basket of grain I had and asked me where in the world I had gleaned. When I told her the man's name was Boaz, she perked up, and a hope began to resurface in her. It was then that I first learned that Boaz was a distant relative. Naomi told me to be sure and do just as he said and to only glean in his field. She told me that, since he was a relative, I would be well taken care of. So, that's what I did—every day. Whenever the harvesters were out in the field, I was right there following behind, gathering what was left. Then, every night, I would take back to Naomi all that I had gleaned.

People often ask me if I missed home during this time or if I ever regretted my decision to stay with Naomi. I must admit, I did think of home a lot—believe me. The work I was doing was hard, and I really missed my family and friends. But I never regretted what I had done, nor did I ever seriously entertain the idea of going back to Moab. I had come to love Naomi as much as my own mother. There was no way I could just up and leave her. What would have happened to her had I left? Anyway, this was my home now. I had no regrets. But I think Naomi did.

I say that because, one day, Naomi said that it was high time she found a home for me where I would be well taken care of. I assured her that I *was* being taken care of and that a home with her was all I needed. But evidently, she had been bothered by the fact that she had no more sons to give me as a husband so I could have a family and children of my own. So, she began to put the wheels in motion to make that come about.

Naomi had been convinced from day one that it was God who had directed my steps to glean in Boaz's field. And as more and more time passed with nothing happening on that front—me finding a husband, that is—I guess she decided that it was about time Boaz did his duty as a member of the family and took the initiative to redeem

Elimelech's property. You see, it was part of their custom for the nearest family relative to step in as "kinsman-redeemer" and take responsibility for the family members and property of any man who had died. So, Naomi told me to wash and pour perfume all over and dress in my finest clothes. Then I was to go to the threshing floor, and after Boaz had finished eating and drinking and had fallen asleep for the night, I was to go uncover his feet and lay down on the ground next to him. Then, when he woke up and found me at his feet, he would know that we wanted to be redeemed—that he could be our kinsman-redeemer and either marry me himself or find someone else to marry me.

And, yes, before you ask, I did feel awkward doing this. It almost felt as if I was trying to trick Boaz into marrying me. I was so uncomfortable doing what Naomi had instructed me to do. But I was also devoted to Naomi. And besides, to be honest with you, deep down, a husband and children were what I wanted, too. Naomi had told me that this was their custom, and this was what needed to be done. In the end, I trusted her completely and did exactly as she told me, saying exactly what she told me to say.

As you can imagine, when Boaz woke up, he was more than just a little surprised! But he seemed pleased as well. From his comments, I gathered that he had already been thinking along those lines but thought I wouldn't have any interest in him because he was a lot older. He said there was one relative who was closer and who, by law, was to be given the first chance to redeem Elimelech's property. He told me to stay the night, and the next morning he would talk with this other man. So, just before dawn, Boaz loaded me down with grain once again and sent me back home to Naomi.

When I got home, I found Naomi on pins and needles, pacing the floor. She was so anxious to hear how everything went. And I do mean everything! I told her what had happened and what Boaz had said he would do. She relaxed a bit and told me not to worry. She assured me that Boaz was well-known as a man who kept his word, and he undoubtedly would follow through on this matter until it was all settled.

Naomi was right. I found out later that Boaz had left shortly after I did to go to the city gate and get this matter taken care of. He had wasted no time! As soon as this other relative showed up, and the minute he could get ten elders together to serve as witnesses, Boaz began explaining the situation to the man—that the property belonging to Elimelech had now passed into Naomi's hands, and, being the closest relative, he had first chance to redeem it. This man was all set to do so until he learned that I was included in the bargain. Once he found that out, he backed out. I'm not sure if it was because I was a Moabite—a "foreigner"—or if it was the fact that our first son would be able to reclaim the land. Perhaps he didn't want to have to share any of his property. Anyway, to make his decision official, he took off his sandal in front of everyone and gave it to Boaz. Doing that was their way of saying, "It's yours." So that left Boaz the legal heir.

Shortly after that, we were married, and nine months later, we had a son. Oh, you should have seen Naomi's face then! My heart was truly blessed to be able to present her with a grandson. She lived with us and helped care for Obed. And finally, my family was complete. Naomi was right—God does take care of those who trust Him.

My dear friend, as I reflect on my life, the one thing I was most thankful for was that Naomi made sure to introduce me to the One True God. Had I not come to a full understanding of and belief in Him, nothing in my life would have been the same. I'm sure of that. I owe my life to the faithfulness of Naomi, who knew God loved and cared for me—a Moabite girl—even in my ignorance. I learned that, even before I knew Him, He loved me.

I have come to learn that one of the hardest things people struggle with is in their obedience to God. But that is so vital. All I can say about that is this: when you feel God is leading you down an uncertain path, trust Him.

Obey Him and follow Him. Unlike us, He can see what lies ahead, and He has only your best interest at heart. I could not imagine a happier ending to my life—wife to Boaz, mother to Obed, daughter to Naomi, accepted among the Israelites, and most importantly, blessed beyond measure by God Himself.

Always remember that God's ways and timing are different from ours. Just because I can summarize my life's story in the few short pages of this letter doesn't mean my life's situation changed that quickly. I spent a long time as a widow with a broken heart before God brought me to Boaz. Be patient. It will very often be months or even years before your situation is turned around. Just keep holding on and trusting God. Besides, having or getting everything in an instant is very overrated. Usually, the longer you wait for something, the greater the joy and satisfaction when you get it.

My friend, I need to think about bringing this letter to a close. It's my prayer that through it, you have gotten to know me, my story, and, more importantly, my God. He blesses us so much more than we deserve. Keep looking to Him and trust Him always.

Love,
Ruth

Discussion/Reflection Questions

The following questions are designed to help you dig a bit more and think a little deeper. As the saying goes, "You will get out of this what you put into this." Don't short-change yourself. Take a few minutes to reflect on each of these questions and jot down your thoughts. If you are participating in a group study, consider sharing your discoveries with others in your small group.

You will notice reflection question #6 gives you the opportunity to write a return letter. This exercise is greatly encouraged because it will help you make a more personal connection.

1. It has been said that "friendship weaves lives together." That was certainly the case with Naomi and Ruth. Many women today struggle with their mother-in-law relationship and most certainly don't develop a true friendship as Naomi and Ruth were able to do. What may have caused Ruth and Naomi to move beyond friction to harmony?

2. Naomi allowed Ruth to see firsthand her ongoing relationship with God—all the hurts, fears, tears, and anger, as well as the times of blessing. When you're going

through challenging times, how inclined are you to feel that your thoughts and questions about God or your anger towards Him should be kept from everyone—even family or friends? Why?

3. Ruth advises us to be patient and allow God time to work in our lives. In our microwave world, how hard is it to stop or even slow down to wait on God? What things should we be doing as we wait?

4. Naomi's plan to get Ruth a husband may have seemed strange to Ruth (and to us!). Yet, she did exactly as she had been told, trusting Naomi's experience and knowledge. What do you think may have happened if Ruth had refused to follow Naomi's advice and done things her own way? How important is it for us to listen to and follow the advice of Christian parents or older role models we trust? Why?

5. In Ruth's story, we learn that Boaz had an outstanding reputation and had proven to be a man who could be counted on. What does it take to develop a good reputation? What can be done if a person's reputation is less than stellar?

6. Now, it's your turn. Write a letter back to Ruth.

Write whatever you want. This is your personal letter to her. Some suggestions: Thank her for sharing her story. Tell her what sharing her story meant to you. Ask her questions. Let her know in what ways you can identify with her. Be imaginative!

NOTE: If you would like your letter to Ruth to be considered for publication in a future book, you may do so by emailing a copy directly to: cheryllelliott@gmail.com.

You will be contacted personally if your letter is chosen to be represented in the book.

Please note that the deadline for receiving these letters is June 1, 2024 for printing in a book to be tentatively released the fall of 2024.

About the Author

From crayons and coloring books to pencils, pens, and lined paper, Cheryl has thrived on writing and journaling. She is happiest with pen and paper in hand. Well, that and knitting needles!

In kindergarten, Cheryl was introduced to the wonderful world of teaching. And, having three younger siblings, she had her own built-in classroom full of students—sometimes willing, sometimes not. She fell in love with her fifth-grade teacher and declared during that year a teacher is what she wanted to be. That dream lasted until her senior year in high school when she visited the campus of Johnson University (formerly Johnson Bible College) in Knoxville, Tennessee. That weekend visit changed everything, and she made the decision to enroll to study Bible and take secretarial courses. Two weeks following graduation, she began working as a graphic designer for a non-profit mission organization (Mission Services Association), where she remained until early retirement in 2017. But the desire to teach was always there.

Throughout the years, Cheryl has taught every age group, from babies and toddlers through multi-age women's small groups. She loves writing her own studies, always trying to keep the creative juices flowing to bring God's Word to life in a fresh and imaginative way.

Cheryl was born and grew up in southern Indiana. She has now resided in beautiful East Tennessee for over forty years. Since her heart lies in both states, she considers herself a "Hoosier Volunteer." Widowed in 2008, Cheryl and her husband were blessed beyond measure with three children. Over the years, two children-in-law and four grandchildren have been added to the family unit, with a fifth treasured granddaughter already tucked away in heaven.